Books by Laura Bradbury

my

grape

cellar

my grape cellar

LAURA BRADBURY

Published by Grape Books

Copyright © 2019 Laura Bradbury
Print Edition

Paperback ISBN: 978-0-9959173-8-5
eBook ISBN: 978-0-9959173-7-8

Visit: www.laurabradbury.com

This book is dedicated to Robert,
the honest-to-God
wine cellar whisperer.

contents

Le meilleur vin n'est pas nécessairement le plus cher,
mais celui qu'on partage.
—Georges Brassens

chapter one

NOVEMBER 2005

The pen I held was poised to sign on the dotted line to seal the purchase of an eighteenth-century apartment within the medieval walls of Beaune. It was a Mont Blanc fountain pen, of course, lent to me by the notary overseeing the sale. These seemed to be *de rigeur* for notaries everywhere in France.

The notary in question—not our usual soused specimen, who worked out of Nuits-Saint-Georges, but a chic one in Dijon who represented the sellers—raised a long pale finger and said, "*Attendez.*"

Wait? Wait for what? I glanced at Franck. His almond eyes were narrowed. He looked as baffled as I felt.

We had agreed with the sellers on a price. We wanted to buy this apartment to turn it into our third vacation rental in Burgundy. I couldn't imagine what we needed to wait for. I breathed deeply to curb my impatience, and my nostrils filled with the scent of ink that permeated the study.

"What's the problem?" I asked finally.

The maître pointed at a piece of paper, one among hundreds, on the desk in front of him. He looked at his client, the seller. "We forgot about the cellar."

"Cellar?" Franck echoed. In Burgundy, the most prestigious winemaking region in the world, according to Burgundians anyway, a cellar could mean only one thing: a wine cellar.

The notary inhaled sharply. "Yes. The cellar is offered with the apartment, but I see here it is not included in the sale price."

That made no sense. "I don't remember seeing any cellar," I said.

"We definitely didn't," Franck agreed. "I would have remembered. I never forget a wine cellar."

It was meant as a joke, but it flew right over le maître's head, which was capped with a meticulously trimmed fringe of white hair.

"There is a cellar?" Our realtor, sitting to my left, twisted the heavy gold bangle on her wrist and eyed the seller. "What is this? Why was I never informed about a cellar? This is most irregular."

It was no wonder she didn't take the surprise well. She was seconds away from earning her commission.

"To be honest, I forgot all about it," the seller said, a sheepish look fleeting across his features. Our apartment-to-be was the last holding in this man's venture into property development. He had bought a grand old house in the medieval heart of Beaune and converted it into seven apartments. I got the distinct impression, however, that he wanted nothing more than to wash his hands of the entire business and return to the leisurely life of a civil servant.

"It's filled with coal," he said. "I didn't even go all the way down the stairs, but I suppose I must sell it." He sighed. "I want out of this building."

"Maybe you can just throw it in with the sale price," our realtor suggested. Franck and I eyed her with respect. It was a ballsy suggestion. Nobody gave away a wine cellar in the center of Beaune for free.

Beneath the cobblestone streets was a second town—a honeycomb of wine cellars several stories underground. It was an entirely parallel system of real estate and, because no one made vaulted cellars anymore, one that had increasing value.

The notary shook his head slightly at the seller. If he was trying to convey his objection with subtlety, he failed. Our realtor had warned us a few days earlier that the seller worked for the much-despised tax department of the French government. This meant there could be no under-the-table dealing, as there usually was in French real estate transactions. It also made me surmise that as much as he wanted out of the building, the seller was a pragmatic, money-loving man to his core.

He frowned. "I can't do that. It would be insanity." It seemed to me that one thing this man could use in his life was a bit of insanity.

"You do want to walk away from this building after today, don't you?" Our realtor was a born negotiator.

"Yes, but free? I just can't in good conscience do that... I just can't."

Our realtor licked her lips. "How much then?" She didn't even look at Franck or me to see if we were on board.

The seller chewed his lip.

"I suggest five thousand Euro," she said, then finally glanced to us with a question in her eyes.

Franck and I exchanged a look, then nodded back.

"It's worth far more than that." The seller frowned.

"Then keep it." Our realtor smoothed a strand of dyed blonde hair into her chignon.

"How about ten thousand?" he asked.

I shook my head. "We can't pay any more than five thousand." It wasn't that I didn't want the cellar; it was that we had no budget for a cellar, not even the five thousand we had just recklessly agreed to. "We hadn't exactly planned on buying a wine cellar today."

"Even that..." Franck pursed his lips. His eyes flicked to mine for a second. He thought I was negotiating and joining in what he considered to be prime sport. In reality I was just being blunt.

Our realtor gave us a wink behind the seller's head.

"What do you think?" the seller asked his notary. It wasn't a very sensible thing to do as the notary had a vested interest in completing the sale and getting his percentage of the transaction, *tout de suite*.

"I want you to walk out of here today with no weight on your shoulders," the notary said, adopting an expression of concern. "I think you should sell it for five thousand. After all, what are you going to do with a moldy old cellar full of coal?"

The seller shuddered. "Nothing."

Maybe he didn't know what to do with it, but I fancied Franck and I would. The fact that we hadn't actually seen it, and that the mere idea of it made the seller shrink in disgust, flitted through my mind, only to be dismissed. In minutes we would own some of that prized real estate under the streets of Beaune, real estate I had never imagined could be mine.

The notary took the document in front of me, scribbled something on it, wrote his initials, and slid it back. I signed, then passed it to Franck.

And just like that, we owned a wine cellar.

chapter two

The next day Franck and I went to our new apartment after we dropped off Charlotte and Camille at their Catholic school in Beaune.

It had taken only a year at Saint-Coeur for them to become perfect little French Catholics. They spoke French entirely without accents and knew the Hail Mary backward and forward.

The seller had bequeathed an enormous fistful of keys to Franck. When asked which ones opened our apartment and the cellar, he told us impatiently, "I haven't a clue. Just try them all." From the tapping of his right foot on the notary's oak floor, it was clear he couldn't get out of that office and toward his freedom fast enough.

However, having lived in Burgundy for over a year, I was growing used to the more chaotic course of business here compared to in Canada.

We climbed the polished wooden stairs to our apartment, my hand sliding over the smooth banister. On the landing above, Franck tried several keys from the wad before finding one that opened the door.

He grabbed my hand and gave it a squeeze before we went inside. "Are you ready for this?"

"When am I not ready to start something new?" I grinned. I loved beginning things—having big ideas and setting them in motion was my strength.

We stepped into the dark space. I opened the huge white shutters in the kitchen, bathing the empty quarters in silver winter light. I examined the rooftops across the courtyard, a mishmash of centuries-old buildings that fit into one another like a difficult puzzle. The twitching tail of a cat snoozing on the tiled peak across the courtyard caught my eye. I hadn't noticed him at first because he was the same metal gray as the sky.

Franck slid the apartment key off the ring so we could distinguish it from the rest. "We probably have the double of everyone's key from this building," he said, his lips quirking. "We could go on quite the crime spree if we were so inclined."

I laughed, knowing full well that neither of us was so inclined. We preferred working hard and making our money by sharing this region of France with people from around the world.

I looked around, trying to evaluate how much it would cost to do up the kitchen. For the moment it was completely bare—no fridge, oven, counter, or anything. In Canada, houses and apartments are generally sold with appliances. Not so in France. We were starting from scratch. It was a bare room with an exposed stone wall on one side that boasted enormous old French windows.

The wiring and plumbing outlets stuck out here and there from the drywall. This blank slate was not necessarily a bad thing. After renovating a sixteenth-century winemaker's cottage in the village where Franck's family had lived for generations, we had looked long and hard for a second property to turn into another vacation rental in Beaune, the picturesque medieval town that was the heart of winemaking in Burgundy.

We had toured many apartments with beautiful bones but truly heinous renovations—like a pony wall of glass blocks in the middle of a room with massive oak beams. Ironically, many young French people chased after super modern decor, whereas North Americans like me usually couldn't get enough of the authentically ancient.

We explored the space, opening the shutters as we went. In the living room, we stood in mute disgust as we observed its cheap textured wallpaper emblazoned with Japanese characters. Let's just say it was not a harmonious pairing with the original marble fireplace and detailed plaster moldings.

"Why?" I said to myself as much as my husband. "All I can think when I look at this wallpaper is 'Why?'"

"I kinda like it." From the mischievous glint in his eyes, I knew he was trying to get a rise out of me—his preferred pastime.

I pinched his arm. "Mark my words. This wallpaper will be the first thing to go, even if I have to scrape it off with my fingernails. It's heinous."

The seller had thankfully left the bones of the bourgeois house intact. This included huge windows that flooded every room in natural light and wooden plank floors with a patina that could have come only with the passage of time.

I wandered into the first bedroom as Franck inspected the wiring and plumbing rough-ins in the bathroom. I glanced up at the lofty ceiling, where intricate plaster cornices took my breath away. Thank God the seller had had the good sense to paint the ceilings matte white. Small mercies.

I leaned out of the now-open window. It was cold outside, but the fresh air was welcome. The music of bells drifted down the narrow cobblestone street. They sounded different from the booming peal associated with the church bells in the village of Villers-la-Faye, where we lived. These bells were far more delicate.

Franck came up behind me and slid his hands around my waist. He learned forward and kissed the nape of my neck. I shivered.

"Where are those bells coming from?" I asked as he wrapped his arms around my torso.

He didn't answer for a few seconds. "I think there's a convent up the street. It must be time for the nuns to pray."

It made total sense. Somehow their tune was more feminine than most church bells I knew.

"Do you think people will want to rent this place?" Franck murmured in my ear.

I leaned my head back against his shoulder. He'd asked this question about every property we had considered converting into a vacation rental. Because he'd grown up in Burgundy, he somehow failed to perceive the magic and beauty that drew tourists from all over the world. For Franck, Burgundy was just home. Plain, unglamorous home. He always needed the reassurance that only I, as a foreigner to France, could give him.

"I know they will. Beaune is ridiculously charming, like walking into a fairy tale or something. Don't forget the famous vineyards all around us, and the incredible food that goes with them, and all the stunning winemaking villages, and the fact that UNESCO wants to make this whole area a World Heritage Site—"

Franck spun me around and cut me off with a kiss. "Nice job," he said. "You're very convincing."

From our adventure renovating the cottage the year before, I knew I would have to reassure him on this point again. Just like with La Maison de la Vieille Vigne—what we now called the cottage behind Franck's family home in Villers-la-Faye—I would have to do it throughout the project.

Reassuring was easy now, at the beginning of this Beaune apartment project.

"It's perfect," I said. "Truly."

"I'm trying to estimate how long it will be before it's ready to rent. Even with the kitchen installation, this shouldn't take nearly as long as the cottage."

I nodded in agreement. "This place is in way better shape."

The cottage had been a real ruin, and we'd had to redo everything, including the electricity, plumbing, and roof, from scratch. I thought about it for a second. "I think for this apartment all we need is five months."

"You think we can start taking bookings for March?"

"End of March." I gave myself a little leeway. "Let's say beginning of April."

Franck nodded. "Okay."

"Now, let's see this mysterious cellar of ours," I said, giving him a little peck. I dragged him out of the room to the kitchen, then into the hall. "We haven't finished getting ourselves into trouble yet."

"Buying a cellar sight unseen? Laura, our second name is Trouble."

chapter three

I stood on the sidewalk outside the apartment building as Franck kneeled on the ground and tried key after key in the metal panel that was set into the sidewalk.

Every few minutes a car bumped along on the cobblestones, the driver slowing down and eyeing us narrowly as though we were trying to execute some sort of heist. I felt like shouting at them, "We bought this cellar fair and square!"

"Everyone's so suspicious here," I said.

Franck kept trying the keys as he muttered a constant stream of swear words, known in French as *les gros mots* or literally "the big words." Having mastered the metal panel in the narrow sidewalk, Franck was working to unlock two wooden doors only a few feet high and recessed into the side of the building.

"That's the Burgundian stare," Franck reminded me, not even glancing up. "Living here, you can't let it bother you. Remember?"

I did, but at times like this I couldn't help but be exasperated at the general mood of suspicion that reined. On the whole Burgundian people were incredibly nice and welcoming, but only *after* they knew who you were and what you were up to.

"Stare back at them in the same way," Franck said. "Look even more suspicious if you can manage it."

That's exactly what I did to the next few drivers that passed. With my arms across my chest, I met their beady, narrowed stares with an aggressive glare of my own. Without exception they all turned their heads away.

"It's working!" I crowed in triumph.

"You see?" Franck said, still unable to unlock the wooden doors. "Now, if only I could find the right key for this cellar."

"This is ridiculous." I leaned against the building. "He could have at least gone through the keys and given you only the ones we needed. I would bet there are keys in that wad that are completely useless."

"I would bet most of them are useless," Franck said. "He just couldn't be bothered."

"Did you consider," I said slowly as an idea dawned, "that maybe the cellar key isn't even on there?"

"Bordel." Franck looked up with a grimace. "No, I hadn't, and I was better off before considering that, thank you very much, *chérie.*"

Ignoring his harassed tone, I said simply, *"De rien."* He was most welcome.

A few seconds later Franck shouted *"Ouais!"* I watched in disbelief as the metal doors fell open. The scent of mildew and confined space wafted up.

"Yay!" I coughed. "But going down there will be murder for my allergies."

"I'll go first." Franck opened the wooden doors above the metal doors in the sidewalk.

At times like this my overactive imagination was my worst enemy. I began to envision what lurked in the dark at the bottom of the stone steps. "Yes, please."

Luckily, Franck had thought to bring a flashlight. He flipped on the beam as he bent over and began to feel out the first step.

I decided to wait and see if he arrived safely at the bottom before I began to venture down.

I peered inside, trying to make out what Franck's flashlight was illuminating. From the smell of the cellar, I wouldn't have been surprised to find a pack of dragons hibernating down there.

Franck's head disappeared into the obscurity.

"What do you see?" I called.

"Not much." Franck's voice drifted up from below, followed by a muffled expletive.

"What?" My imagination started to get the better of me.

"Nothing to worry about," he called. "I think I just found the old piles of coal…by tripping over and falling into them."

I was starting to rethink going into the cellar at all until it had been checked out. Why had the seller wanted to get rid of it so urgently? Were there *bodies* down there? Surely it was enough if Franck had a look.

"I think it's safe for you to come down," he said. "You should see this."

"You *think* it's safe?"

"Well…it's pretty dark down here. I can't be one hundred percent sure."

"Not reassuring, Franck."

"Come on. We own a cellar now. You have to see it."

"You really think so?"

"*Viens!*" He laughed. "It's completely fine."

Despite that, I was not feeling particularly confident.

"Don't worry," he added. "I'm at the bottom of the stairs, so if you fall, I'll catch you."

With all the cheese and fresh baguettes I'd been enjoying since moving to France, this felt like an optimistic promise, but I couldn't chicken out.

Franck was right. This wine cellar was ours now. I tended to be the visionary in our relationship. We were a team, and I would be letting us down if I didn't brave the dark below. I needed to see it to know what we were going to do with it.

"Here goes," I muttered and ducked my head under the huge stone plinth at our entrance to the subterranean city beneath the sidewalks of Beaune.

"Just go slowly, and feel your way down with your feet," Franck advised.

He pointed the flashlight beam on the steps in front of me so I could make out where I was going. I could see a drop-off on either side of the massive stone slabs. If I fell, I had no idea where I would land—or on what.

Maybe it was better to have no idea, because in the light of the beam I could make out the network of spider webs that carpeted the stairs. I'd never been afraid of spiders, but at the same time I didn't particularly relish the idea of meeting the specimens that had made this cellar their home.

I felt something crunch under my foot and tried very hard not to think about what it was.

I arrived at the bottom with an *ouf* against Franck's chest.

The mustiness was even more overwhelming down here, and it competed with the bitter smell of what I assumed was the coal. I shuffled a bit on the ground. It felt dirty underfoot.

Franck reached for me and gave me a kiss, missing my mouth by a few centimeters in the dark. "A new adventure!" He sounded happy.

He took a step away, and for a second I lost him in the pitch-blackness. Then his face appeared in front of me, illuminated by the flashlight under his chin so the sharp planes of his cheekbones made him look like a ghoul. "Woo-hoo," he hooted.

"That's not a very good ghost sound."

"Is so."

I tugged the flashlight away from him and made a ghostly noise of my own. "Woo-hoo."

"That sounded exactly the same as mine," Franck protested.

"Mine was far more convincing. It's not your fault. Don't forget I had years of practicing at Halloween." Franck, having grown up in France where Halloween wasn't a thing, could never hope to compete with me.

I returned the flashlight. "Anyway, we really don't need to do that," I said. "It's plenty frightening down here without pretending we're ghouls."

"True," he said. He illuminated the space with the flashlight, but its feeble beam didn't penetrate far.

"The first thing we need down here is some decent light."

"Agreed, but there's only one problem."

"No electricity?" I guessed.

"Right." As he moved the flashlight around, still exploring, I caught a glimpse of stones above us that were black with soot and covered with spider webs.

"It has a proper vaulted ceiling," I said wonderingly. The

stones formed an arching arc. Vaulted ceilings in wine cellars were not only beautiful but also coveted; the more vaults there were, the older the cellar tended to be. The vault alone probably dated our cellar to before the eighteenth century.

The flashlight caught something else.

I grabbed his arm. "Is that a pillar?"

"I think so." I could hear his excitement matched my own. He slowly ran the light up the lines of vaults on either side of the pillar. "Look. It supports the two arches. The pillar means our cellar must date to the fifteenth century, or maybe even the fourteenth."

We both knew enough about old cellars to know that after the Middle Ages, stonemasons had devised ways to build self-supporting arches that didn't rely on pillars.

My heart accelerated. The allure of old things never failed to get it pounding. "Do you think it could even be Roman?"

I felt rather than saw Franck shrug beside me. "Could be. One thing is certain. If we dug down from here, we'd find Roman cellars."

It always amazed me to think that beneath Beaune was the foundation of an ancient Roman town. At that moment half of the main place in the center of Beaune, La Place Carnot, was being ripped up to install new lights. Work was progressing slowly and carefully as they had discovered, *bien sûr*, a Roman bathhouse under the sidewalk. I could never walk by without stopping to peer into the hole.

"*Chouette*," I murmured, basically the French word for *awesome*. All this history, now ours, struck me in the form of an overpowering need to return our cellar to its former glory.

The superstitious streak in me felt it couldn't have fallen into our hands by accident. We were meant to be its caretakers.

"How could they have used this place to store coal?" I wondered out loud at such a travesty.

"Maybe heat was more important than wine at some point in history… Nah." Franck corrected himself. "I can't imagine anybody living in the heart of Beaune and not having a significant wine collection."

"We have to bring this place back to what it was," I said, my voice ripe with the fervor of the converted. I had forgotten all about the spiders.

"I don't think it's ever had electricity," Franck reminded me. "Or running water. I think we can improve on only what was here, even what was here originally."

"Okay. Fair point. Better but still honoring what it was. You know what I mean?"

"It's going to take a lot of work."

As the person who executed the bulk of our plans, I knew Franck was already thinking through the practicalities. "We need to bring in electricity and water, and get rid of all this coal, and clean the rockwork, and maybe dig the ground down by a foot or so."

I heard the sound of his shoe kicking the soil at our feet. "I think this place has been filled in over the years."

I considered this. It sounded daunting. From our experience breathing life into the winemaker's cottage the year before, I knew the work we could forecast now was most likely only the tip of the iceberg.

"Do you think we can renovate this and the apartment at the same time?" I asked.

"I'd like to say yes, but—"

"You don't think so." I finished his thought.

"Not if we're planning to rent out the apartment as of March."

"We have to, financially speaking." I hated being the killjoy, but our budget was, sadly, finite. "We know we can earn revenue from the apartment, whereas the cellar... We'll have to be a bit more creative."

There was such an influx of guests at our two vacation rentals in Villers-la-Faye and Magny-les-Villers, little winemaking villages just minutes from Beaune, that we knew we could fill the apartment with the overflow without much advertising.

Franck sighed. "I guess you're right." The regret in his voice reflected that in my heart. I knew we were both impatient to get started on the cellar.

"We'll do this," I reassured him and myself. "There is no way I'm passing up having a wine cellar for tastings and parties."

We had heard so many stories from Franck's grandmother, la Mémé, about the legendary parties that happened in Burgundy's cellars, particularly during World War Two when there was a curfew. I wanted some of *that* in our lives.

Besides, after a year of living in Burgundy, we had accumulated an impressive collection of wine from our friends, family, and outings to the local winemakers. Plus, we still had all the bottles we had been gifted at our wedding in Nuits-Saint-Georges—tons of magnums and jeroboams of Burgundy's finest *crus*. Right now it was stored in the cellar at one of our vacation rentals, but it wasn't a proper underground cellar like this one.

Still, I knew I was the taskmaster in the couple who had to set priorities and a schedule for the work. Franck would be the first to admit he was easily sidetracked.

"The apartment first," I reiterated. I didn't relish my designated role at that moment.

Franck took a deep breath. "That makes sense. Although you know me; I'd rather start with the cellar."

"The apartment is going to be great, too," I reminded him. "It's a fantastic project."

He didn't protest further; he didn't need to. I knew it was the cellar, not the apartment, that had captured his heart.

He turned to me in the dark and managed to find my lips with his. We kissed for a while until my nostrils began to itch and I let loose an impressive string of sneezes—a not-so-subtle way for my body to let me know I'd had enough of the mold and dust and whatever else was lurking among the stone columns.

"I'm going to head up," I said when I caught my breath. "We can continue that kiss back home."

Franck tried to light my way with the flashlight as best he could, and he remained at the bottom to "catch me" if I fell backward.

I had to bend almost in half to climb onto the sidewalk and avoid whacking my head on the massive stone across the passageway.

On the sidewalk again, I blinked like a mole at the winter daylight that seemed to burn my eyes. I brushed off the long strands of spider webs that clung to my jacket and peered up at the second-story windows of our new apartment.

By the time Franck joined me, my head was buzzing with ideas for how to attack the renovations up there.

"We need to call Luc and see if his schedule is clear enough to help us," I said. Franck was on his knees again closing and locking the metal panel in the sidewalk.

"It'll be clear."

"But remember how busy he gets—"

"I'll serve him enough wine for it to be clear."

Franck and I had formed quite a bond with Luc over the months we'd spent rushing against the clock to renovate the vintner's cottage, including taking care of a drunk electrician and destroying the old kitchen with a sledgehammer and a lot of glee. Luc had become one of our best friends.

Franck stood up and brushed off his jeans. I held him still while I removed the biggest clumps of dirt and webs.

He caught my eyes. "So you're sure the cellar has to wait?" It was more a confirmation than a question.

I nodded. "Unfortunately, *oui*, but think of it this way: it will motivate us to get the apartment done quickly. The cellar will be our reward for getting the apartment up and earning money."

Franck nodded again, but he didn't look entirely convinced.

chapter **four**

Thank God neither Franck nor I could predict the future, because in the end, it took us almost two years to start work on the wine cellar.

We had great excuses, *bien sûr*.

Despite the fact that we thought we'd gained so much experience renovating the winemaker's cottage, the last few weeks of work on the Beaune apartment (which we ended up naming Le Relais du Vieux Beaune) were an absolute sprint to get it ready for the first group of guests.

After that the guests began arriving nonstop. We'd been right about the popularity of an apartment within the medieval walls of Beaune—it was a runaway hit.

Now, two years in, as I wandered around the quiet apartment, I reflected that the short-term pain and stress had been worth it. We had created something beautiful and welcoming.

I went to the main bedroom and flung open the shutters. The bedroom's soft blue walls were immediately suffused with the orange glow of late October.

The paint color was a vast improvement over the old Japanese character wallpaper that covered the walls of both bedrooms and the living room. It accentuated the exquisite medallion on the ceiling that was set off by an antique chandelier I had found.

One of my favorite parts of getting the apartment ready was hunting through local *brocantes* to find antiques I loved not only for their patina but also because they just felt right in this stately building.

I'd experienced a complete *coup de foudre* for an amazing armoire from Brittany that now sat against one wall. It had an impressive ancient key, which I embellished even further with a large French tassel of blue threads that matched the walls to perfection. I threaded my fingers through its strands. For the first time ever, I was going to actually *live* here in our magnificent apartment for several weeks.

This room just felt good. It spoke of history and authenticity and calm. I moved to the window again, where I could see the man who was restoring the massive property across the street spreading wet plaster on a wall with a trowel.

I'd met him a few times on the street and had gleaned that he was a highly talented builder. He'd told us the owner of the house, his boss, was a baron of some sort who hailed from the Loire and owned several prestigious vineyards and castles throughout France.

The builder's name was Robert, and he and Franck had become buddies. The twenty-five-year difference in age between them didn't seem to bother them a bit.

Franck was back and forth to Beaune from our house in Villers-la-Faye—currently under renovation, which is why we had temporarily taken refuge in the apartment—almost every day. He and Robert had begun to spend a lot of time huddled together, often over a good bottle of wine, hashing out restoration techniques and strategies for our as-yet-untouched wine cellar.

Besides plans to make our wine cellar as welcoming and authentic as the apartment now was, I was also working on a little dream of my own—a third child. Franck, however, was not initially on board with the idea. His reasoning was: We have two healthy children, why roll the dice a third time?

He couldn't understand the feeling I had every time I looked at a portrait of our two daughters or watched them eating crêpes with Franck at the dinner table. Someone was missing. I didn't know who yet, but I knew in my heart our family wasn't complete.

Seeing the families of seven, eight, and nine at the girls' Catholic school didn't help either. Two children just didn't feel like enough.

My longing for a third didn't make financial—or practical—sense, and I had no idea how I would cope with a newborn again now that Camille was almost six and an extremely competent little person well past bottles and diapers. Still, I could not shake the feeling that I wasn't done.

That spring, as my thirty-fifth birthday hovered on the horizon, I began to suspect my desire for a third was not leaving. It defied logic, but so did many of the best things I'd done in my life.

So I convinced Franck. Well, to be honest, when it came to his contribution, he didn't take much convincing.

I was into my third trimester now, and like my previous two pregnancies, I was huge. I moved around like a galleon with full ballast.

The baby gave me a solid kick in the ribs. He or she was growing strong, and the kicks were starting to hurt. I rubbed my pregnant belly. The baby was the second reason we hadn't gotten to the cellar renovations as quickly as we'd hoped.

I glanced down at the gorgeous oak desk and chair we had found at a *vide-grenier* in the village of Chaux. I sighed with pleasure. I would set up my office right here.

On second thought... I eyed the table and chair warily. Would my stomach fit?

I was so thankful to be here in the peace and simplicity of Le Relais du Vieux Beaune. It was a welcome respite from living in the construction zone of our house in Villers-la-Faye—not the rental cottage we had renovated shortly after moving to France but the bigger house we had bought to live in, which we had named La Maison des Chaumes.

The walls between the living room and kitchen at La Maison des Chaumes were being ripped out. When I'd last been there, an exposed electrical cable hung from the ceiling in the middle of the living room. Thank God we had created this lovely apartment to escape to, because I had had it with tradesmen arriving at seven in the morning, not to mention having no door on the bathroom and drywall dust everywhere.

While Franck had all the workers at our house and within his circumference of wine and influence, we decided to start work on the cellar, too. After dropping the girls at school with the nuns, Franck had deposited me here in Beaune with our suitcases while he went back to Villers-la-Faye to oversee and, because Franck was Franck, work alongside the tradesmen.

I flopped on the queen-size bed, only to remember that when the baby was on top of my lungs, I couldn't breathe. I flipped to my side. My thoughts had been centered mostly on pregnancy in the past few months, but now that I was here, just above our *cave*, they went straight to the diamond in the rough two floors below. I couldn't wait to find out what it would become.

I must have fallen asleep—something that had started happening before I'd even realized I was pregnant. Franck's voice in my ear woke me up. "*Âllo,* sleeping beauty. Do you want to come and see your wine cellar?"

I groaned and stretched. I didn't take cat naps when I wasn't pregnant, but now I felt like I never wanted to get up. Pregnancy at almost thirty-five was a different kettle of fish than in my twenties. I wanted nothing more than to curl up and drift off again. Few things could have forced me to get up off the comfortable mattress, but seeing the wine cellar was one of them.

Franck kissed my temple, then left the room as I sat up and swiveled my legs out of bed. He reappeared with my boots and, without saying a word, knelt at my feet to slide them on and lace them.

"*Merci,*" I murmured, stifling a yawn. They were the most impractical shoes for the third trimester. I couldn't bend over anymore to do them up, but they were soft leather, and I loved them.

"It's the least I can do." Franck smiled up at me.

We made our way to the sidewalk, and I immediately noticed the light from the cellar glowing up the stairs. "Wow." I turned to Franck. "I think I left my sunglasses in Villers."

"That's a shame," he said, helping me down the now well-lit but still crooked steep stone steps. "Because while I was in Villers, Luc installed a light strong enough to burn your retinas."

We reached the bottom, and once the halos and dots in my eyes receded and my pupils shrank to pinpricks, I looked around. Our cellar was paradoxically more promising and more disheartening than I could have imagined.

"Where's Luc?" I asked.

"He escaped to another job," Franck said. "I think maybe he was scared off by the amount of work he saw here."

I could hardly blame our friend. Besides the random piles of coal, there were several decaying piles of garbage left by tradesmen when they had renovated the main building. Charming. They probably thought no one was ever going to come down here. As they had two years earlier, spider webs covered almost every surface.

The cellar reminded me of one of my favorite Edgar Allan Poe short stories, "The Cask of Amontillado," about how a man bricked his enemy behind a stone wall in a wine cellar. I couldn't help thinking our cellar would be the perfect spot to hide such a crime. I found myself hoping nobody had thought of that before me.

The coal had blackened big swaths of the walls and ceiling, and some small patches of rocks were crumbling.

Still, that incandescent lightbulb also revealed cause for hope.

The stone steps down to the cellar were gorgeous slabs of local marble. They were filthy, of course, but in perfect shape, and they created a beautiful entrance under the dirt and soot.

The central pillar was even more beautiful than we'd hoped and arched gracefully down from the vaulted ceiling on either side.

"*Bonjour!*" we heard Robert's voice call down the stairs. "I could see the light from across the street."

"Come down! *Viens!*" Franck and I urged him. It would be excellent to get the opinion of our local wine cellar savant.

He arrived, shook Franck's hand, and gave me the *bises*. Robert's hair was as black as a raven's wing and waved off his brow. I had never seen him with so much as a strand out of place. He pondered the arches and pillar, rubbing his chin, but his eyes were lit with something I couldn't pinpoint.

"This cellar has to date back to the thirteenth century," he said finally.

"Really?" My voice caught on my excitement.

He put his palm on the central pillar. "It's the way this pillar is built that convinces me. The oldest part of the cellar I restored across the street looks the same as this, and it was from around then. The newer part without pillars must have collapsed and been rebuilt a couple of hundred years after. I'm sure the oldest part of that cellar and your cellar must have been joined at some point."

I took a deep breath of Beaune's underworld. I would never tire of its magic.

chapter five

The next morning I walked home to the apartment after dropping off the girls at school. I was pleased I had found a route where we walked almost entirely on the preserved ramparts of the oldest part of the Beaune. The leaves from all the *tilleuls* had fallen in large piles on the cobblestones, and Charlotte and Camille and I loved shuffling through them—one of my favorite things about fall.

As I turned onto the rue Rousseau Deslandes, I caught sight of Franck and Robert huddled together on the sidewalk in front of the metal doors that down led to the cellar. They were hinged open, as was one of the wooden doors inset in the wall above.

"*Bonjour.*" I hadn't seen Robert yet that morning, so we gave each other *les bises*. I loved having a greeting ritual in France that was warm and everyone implicitly understood.

"*Bonjour,* Laura." His warm brown eyes shone. "Did you get the girls to school safely?"

"Yes," I said. "*Merci,* and I'm excited because I found a route that goes along the ramparts."

Robert rubbed his hands together. "That is excellent. The fortifications are incredibly well preserved in Beaune. It's a pleasure to see. Do you know how old they are?"

"No," I admitted. I knew they were old, but I couldn't compete with Robert's encyclopedic knowledge of French history.

"The original walls date from Gallo-Roman times, and some parts are still standing."

"Incredible," I murmured.

"Do the girls like Saint-Coeur?"

I nodded. "They do, which is a relief. I wasn't sure how they would do in a Catholic school."

"Why is that?" Robert asked, puzzled.

"I'm not Catholic, and in Canada—"

"Your girls were baptized in the Catholic Church, weren't they?" he interrupted.

I nodded. "*Oui*, I had to promise to do that when Franck and I got married."

Robert shrugged and let out a puff of breath. "Then they are Catholic. No question. Saint-Coeur is a good Catholic school, and there is nothing like a classic Catholic education. They will be taught the right things."

"Like the rosary?" I asked, trying to suppress a smile.

Catholic education was completely foreign to my atheist up-bringing. I had grown accustomed to Charlotte and Camille reciting the rosary when they broke a cup or had a bad dream. That was one thing the school had anchored firmly in their wee little heads. I couldn't laugh, though—it was clear from his intent expression that for Robert, a Catholic education was no laughing matter.

"Of course." Robert frowned. "That and the catechism and everything else. As I said, nothing beats a Catholic education. There can be no question."

That was debatable, but I recognized Robert was a traditional soul, one that French people labeled "Vieille France." One of the pillars of Vieille France was the Catholic Church. Part of me was surprised Franck hit it off with someone so traditional, but then he and Robert had many other things in common: the same enthusiasm and crazy boundless energy and generosity.

"What are you two up to?" I asked, thinking it might be a good idea to change the subject. Franck had gone down to the cellar. "It looks like you're scheming something. Should I be scared?"

Robert brandished a large mechanical thermometer at me with a grin that transformed his stern face entirely.

"What's that?"

"A special cellar thermometer with a built-in memory. We're going to record the temperature readings in the cellar for the next five days. It also records humidity and a score of other useful things."

"Why?" I asked. This seemed to be a frequent question when talking to Robert and Franck. Franck emerged from the cellar just then and gave me a kiss.

"We have to see what we're dealing with down there, you see?" Robert said.

"Right." I knew a constant temperature and high humidity level were crucial for the successful storing and optimal aging of Burgundian wine.

"Then what next, do you think?" I directed this question at Franck because I didn't want to presume Robert would be helping us. "I mean, what work are you going to start on first?"

It was Robert, however, who answered. "We have it all planned out. First we have to dig down to get more ceiling height, then we must put drainage around the edges of the floor, bring in pea gravel to assist in air circulation, then scrape off grime and old stucco from the ceiling vaults and give the stones a good power wash. After that it goes without saying we have to install a railing along one side of those stairs, lighting, wine racks, then a marble tasting table... But we can hammer out those details later."

Thank God. It seemed Robert planned to help us.

"It sounds like you two have it all figured out."

Franck nodded, his smile wide.

Still, my doubts returned. Even with Robert's help, it felt like a lot to take on right now, considering we had two other projects on the go: renovating our house La Maison des Chaumes in Villers-la-Faye and the incubating baby doing a jig in my belly.

"Don't forget I'm having a baby," I reminded them.

"What?" Franck had been studying the thermometer and looked up, distracted.

I pointed to my stomach. "The baby. We have to fit having the baby in there somewhere."

Robert chuckled. "That's nothing! Babies take care of themselves."

Robert's wife had clearly done all the work with his two adult sons.

"Of course we'll be ready for the baby," Franck tried to assure me.

Yet somehow I wasn't convinced. I wanted to stay longer to press home my point, but I was seven months pregnant, and the baby was dancing on my bladder. The bathroom took priority.

That night Franck and I lay in the cool blue bedroom in the apartment. The silvery bells from the nunnery up the street chimed eleven o'clock. Neither of us had drifted off yet.

"It's going to cost a lot of money," I said.

I would have loved to be in a financial position to restore and preserve things like our cellar just for the good of humanity, but we weren't, especially not with our third child's impending arrival.

The baby did a summersault in my stomach as if to thank me for including him or her in the equation.

Franck knew I was talking about the cellar. We spoke in our own shorthand when it was just the two of us.

"I know." He rolled over on his side so we faced each other. He slid his hand over the curve of my stomach and rested it there. "But it seems as though Robert really wants to help us, and he's so knowledgeable and talented. If he's willing to do that, it feels like such a shame to waste his generosity. He doesn't know how long he's going to be posted in Beaune, you know. The baron has châteaux all over France. From what Robert says, he's a capricious sort and could send Robert to the Loire Valley tomorrow."

"*Merde*," I murmured in the dark. "I didn't know that. Then I guess we have to figure out a way the cellar can pay for itself."

We'd use it to store wine, of course. Everything in our basement or cellar in Magny-les-Villers had an alarmingly short shelf life due to Franck's propensity for living in the moment and both of us loving wine, though I had been blameless on the consumption front since learning I was pregnant.

Franck always joked about the village cellar having an "unusually high rate of evaporation," meaning nothing stayed unopened long enough to age. Even if it did, the aging conditions of our makeshift cellar in Magny were far from ideal—wildly varying temperature, with almost no humidity—so any wine left in there didn't age well anyway. Why not enjoy it right away?

"So we'd store wine in the Beaune cellar for us, and for my family when they visit...my parents, two sisters, and brothers-in-law..." I had no idea where my train of thought was going, but somehow it helped to say it out loud.

"Cellar space is always at a premium," Franck said. "Especially in the heart of Beaune. We could rent it to a Beaune winemaker, but then we couldn't use it ourselves, and I'd love to be able to give tastings for friends, family, and guests."

I nodded in the dark, my mind busy.

"Wine cellars are the lifeblood of Burgundy," he added just as the baby did a backflip under Franck's hand. "Whoa!"

Well done, baby. Thanks for reminding your dad you're not just an abstract concept. "I know, right? You can see why I can't forget for a second that this baby is arriving soon."

Franck made a noise of agreement. "It's different for me. It seems like a big deal, but...not, you know? Maybe it's because it's our third. If we don't know what we're doing by now, we never will."

I chuckled. "I remember the night before we went into hospital to have Charlotte, when you stayed up all night trying to memorize everything in that huge baby book."

"That I promptly forgot as soon as Charlotte arrived." Franck's voice was rueful.

"Oh, and how you had to go down to the ER that first night for pain medication because you had a headache, when I couldn't even get out of bed because I'd lost so much blood?"

"Don't remind me." Franck groaned. "It was not my finest hour."

"*D'accord, d'accord.*" I let out a final laugh. "I just want to carve out a little time to prepare ourselves both practically and mentally this time. I feel like there's a tsunami heading toward us with all these renovations and a newborn. Man, we didn't plan this well."

"Since when do we ever plan anything?"

"I try to plan all the time!" I protested.

Franck patted my belly. "I guess you do."

"And you always thwart my efforts."

I knew, I just *knew* Franck was smiling in the dark. "It's one of my favorite hobbies."

I laughed but also gave him a little poke.

"But it's not my fault you got pregnant immediately," he reminded me. "You kept warning me it would take so much longer this time around."

"It's not like you're blameless. You had something to do with this, if you recall."

"Oh, I recall." Franck rolled forward and caught my lips in a long kiss.

We had planned that it would take me six months to a year to get pregnant. I was older, and my mother had taken years to get pregnant with her third. This meant all our scheduled renovations would have been finished by the baby's arrival. However, just like the other two, it happened right out of the gate, so to speak.

I was, of course, incredibly thankful and never took it for granted, but it did leave us—or me, anyway—grappling with our present chaos.

"Back to the cellar." I pulled away from Franck after a time. "We're getting distracted, and we need to figure this out."

"Ah, *ma chère* pragmatist."

I slapped his shoulder lightly to get him to focus. "How can we generate revenue that will justify the money we'll have to invest on its restoration?"

This conversation reminded me of a night many years before Charlotte and Camille were even twinkles in our eyes, when we lay in our apartment in Vancouver, wondering what to do with the ruin we had purchased on an impulse in Burgundy. That night I came up with the idea of turning it into a vacation rental, and that's exactly what we did. Eventually, after some epic ups and downs during the renovations, that once-ruin became our first vacation rental in France: La Maison des Deux Clochers. I'd been a creative thinker then; I had to be a creative thinker now.

We rented our homes in France. Why couldn't we translate this to our wine cellar? It all came out in a rush.

"Why don't we build our racks in such a way that they are in separate compartments, each with an individual gate that shuts and locks over it. We can rent those sections to people who live in Beaune to store personal collections and to our guests who want to store wine in Burgundy between visits."

We welcomed more and more repeat guests who fell in love with Burgundy and kept coming back. Many of them were wine lovers for whom Beaune was like Xanadu. Given the incredible wine-purchasing opportunities, they routinely bought more wine than they could take home. They would no doubt be keen to leave some behind to age for their next visit, or the one after that, or the one after that…

Franck sat up in bed. "That's brilliant! Thank God I have such a clever wife." He leaned over and smothered me with kisses until I protested. Between him and the baby, there wasn't any room to, you know, breathe.

"See? I knew you would do it. We have a plan," Franck said, settling back against his pillow.

"We do," I said. "So don't thwart it, okay?"

He made a dismissive sound. "Of course not."

"And don't forget about the baby."

Franck reached over and patted my stomach one last time. "Never."

chapter six

Two days later Franck burst into the apartment just before lunch as I was typing away at the antique desk in the blue bedroom.

"Robert and I met up on the sidewalk." He was out of breath. He must have run up the stairs. "He's going to take us on a tour of the baron's cellar across the street."

"Now?" I asked.

"*Oui!* Come on!"

I hated to move. I had finally settled in a comfortable position where the baby wasn't kicking my ribs or bladder, but I figured it would be good to see a concrete example of what we were working toward with our cellar.

Robert was waiting for us across the street, looking neat as a pin as he always did, with a massive iron key in his fist. He must have caught me eyeing it. "Nice key, isn't it?"

"Gorgeous." We exchanged looks. We were equally thrilled by objects that contained history.

"Let's go." He was trembling with excitement; he must have been as eager to show us this cellar as if it were his own. Then again, in a way it was. He was the one who had single-handedly restored it.

"This cellar looked like yours before I started working on it a year and a half ago. Well, except several times larger," he said as he led us down the impeccably clean and imposing stone steps. Franck held my hand and helped me along safely. This wasn't unwelcome, as my pregnancy belly threw off my center of balance.

"The mansion above is still a ruin, but this is Beaune," Robert continued without turning around. "The baron considers this cellar the most important part of the building, so *bien sûr* I did it first. Do you know the baron bought this whole building because of the cellar? The house above was an afterthought."

"Really?" I asked, intrigued by the idea that a massive house in the heart of Beaune could be an afterthought.

Before we reached the bottom, Robert flicked on a light. I gasped.

Indirect lights coming from discreet spots illuminated beautiful slabs of old stone on the ground. The cellar went on for as far as I could see, and the vaults were a much larger-scale version of ours.

Little stone insets in the walls framed special bottles of wine, and racks upon racks of bottles framed either side of the pea gravel path we walked on.

"It's incredible," I breathed, looking at Robert with renewed reverence. He was an artist, I realized, who just happened to practice his art in the building trade. "You did all this?"

He nodded, and his eyes lit up with pride. "It was almost as bad as yours when I began."

"Really? I find that hard to believe."

"Well, maybe not *quite* as bad as yours, but not far off."

"That's encouraging." Franck's eyes were sparkling, too. I could catch it even in the dim light.

"I'll help you, *bien sûr*," Robert said. "I'm far from home, and I hate sitting around, unless it's over a bottle of delicious wine and a good meal."

I had been in Burgundy long enough now to not ask *why* Robert was willing to help us. People in France would not lift a finger to help you if they didn't want to, but if they were so inclined, they would move heaven and earth to render assistance.

Even though the timing could have been better, I couldn't deny the fact that with Robert on our side, we were finally in a position to make our cellar dream a reality.

I was helping Charlotte with her homework in the lilac bedroom when we were interrupted by honking and raised voices in the street below.

"What's that, *Maman*?" Charlotte asked, rushing over to the window, not surprisingly grateful for any chance to escape the practice *dictée* I was giving her. Now that she was in grade two, the schoolwork had begun in earnest, and the French did not joke around about traditional learning. Charlotte's looping cursive was already far more elegant than mine.

"I'm not sure I want to know," I said in all honesty. "I think Papa mentioned something about the stonemason coming by. You remember Hugo?" I knew him well from our work together on the cottage, and while I considered him a friend, I also knew he had to be handled like a stick of dynamite. "I should go down," I told Charlotte with a sigh. "Sorry, sweetie. We'll finish up when I get back."

Charlotte grinned. "Can I play Playmobil with Camille?"

"Sure."

As I made my way down the stairs, I could still hear the voices. Try as I might, I couldn't make out if they were happy or fighting. Normally I wouldn't think it possible that a fight could break out so quickly, but then again I knew Hugo.

I rushed through the hall and out the front door onto the rue Rousseau Deslandes.

Franck, Hugo, and Robert all had their heads thrown back and were roaring with laugher. I sighed with relief. Happy voices. But I wondered if Franck had really thought through throwing Robert and Hugo together for the cellar renovation.

I gave both Robert and Hugo *les bises* and answered their many questions about how the baby and I were doing, but I remained slightly on edge.

I knew, as did Franck, that Hugo had recently run into some trouble with the law. He had informed us only the week before that he had earned a three-week suspended prison sentence for attempting to run over a *gendarme*.

"I wasn't really going to run over him, of course," Hugo had explained, his round face ruddy as always and his thick, ox-like build making me think that he was not an enemy you wanted to run into on a dark night. "He just got scared."

"I can't say I blame him," I'd said.

"Though it wouldn't have been the worst thing if I had." The look in Hugo's ice-blue eyes had been glacier cold.

I didn't consider it prudent to enquire further about what his particular beef was with the *gendarme* in question, but I did remember that when we were renovating Maison de la Vielle Vigne the year before and having a terrible time with the Architect of French Monuments, Hugo had growled, "I'm just waiting to see him cross the road one night. I won't hit the brakes, that's for sure."

At the time I had laughed and thought no more of it. After all, Hugo had pretty much summed up the sentiments of everyone working at our winemaker's cottage, suffering the delays of the architect's ridiculous commandments. French bureaucracy was enough to put a pacifist in a murderous frame of mind.

After learning about his suspended prison sentence, though, I realized perhaps Hugo had been deadly serious.

Therein lied the paradox of tradesmen, I thought to myself as I watched Franck, Hugo, and Robert bonding on the sidewalk. I had found through my many months spent on construction sites over the past three years that French tradesmen were just about the most gallant guys you could ever hope to meet.

They would all stop work to shake my hand, and if their hands were dirty, they'd offer me their wrists instead. The ones I knew gave me *les bises*. They were without exception attentive to my opinions and often surprised me with unexpected thoughtfulness, like Auguste, the carpenter at La Maison de la Vieille Vigne.

Not only was he a true artist in woodwork, but also he worked for free for a day installing our IKEA kitchen, even though I knew he had grave objections to what he considered the inferior quality of the materials. At the end of the job I was weepy at the idea of not seeing him every morning. He presented me with a beautiful old key he'd found in the wall at the cottage. Somewhere along the line I had told him I collected antique keys, and he had remembered.

Hugo was the same type of guy. He was hot-blooded (then again, so was my husband), but he was also fiercely loyal and a formidable ally.

I had read a description in a magazine about what makes a typically Burgundian character. In it, Burgundians were described as "loyal, headstrong, and quick to take the gun down from the wall."

That summed it up. The only problem was, when I had chatted with Robert, just the two of us the day before, he had confided that he had been a *gendarme* for years. Even though he had opted for early retirement, he made it clear he had loved his job and felt very strong about law and order.

Franck, as far as I knew, wasn't aware of this, and he had thrown together these two men—the criminal and the policeman—on our cellar project.

I shook my head as the men descended into the cellar. This could be a very bad idea.

chapter seven

I was waiting for Franck to come upstairs, but when it happened, he wasn't alone. Brushing off cobwebs and laughing at shared jokes, Franck had brought Robert and Hugo for *un pétit apértif*.

I inwardly groaned. I wanted to be gracious, but it was a school night, and I was seven months pregnant. All I wanted to do was put on my dressing gown and watch a trashy téléfilm on TF1.

Franck tried to be respectful of the fact I didn't want guests with us every hour of every day but also insisted that long Burgundian *apértifs* were simply the way business was done here.

I was beginning to see that as much as I hated to lose my evenings, he was probably right. Gratitude for Robert and Hugo, without whom we couldn't renovate the cellar at all, warred with the fatigue of my third trimester. I was an introvert, the polar opposite of my extroverted husband. Whereas he recharged his batteries by being around others, I could charge mine only by spending time alone.

Besides, tonight there was the added question of whether a conversation—or fight—about the law would erupt between Hugo and Robert. It was surely just a matter of time. That issue was bound to crop up, and I didn't particularly want it to be in our kitchen.

Luckily dinner was more or less ready. I had a *roti de porc* bubbling on the stove that I had flambéed in calvados. All I needed to do was add prunes and apples to the sauce a few minutes before eating. Given the normal length of *apértifs* here in Burgundy, however, I didn't think that would be anytime soon.

Franck sat them around the table. Charlotte wandered in in her rainbow pajamas, asking when dinner was ready, but when she saw the tradesmen, her blue eyes lit up. She ran back into the den to tell Camille the good news. *Apértifs* always meant putting out snacks the girls loved: little rounds of *saucisson*, cubes of Comté cheese, cheese twists, pretzels, and peanuts.

The girls returned, both clutching their favorite stuffies— Charlotte a large, terrifying-looking baby doll she called "Princess Baby," and Camille a stuffed lamb named "Mouton-y," her French spin on "lambie."

They gave Robert and Hugo *les bises*, and Hugo wasted no time in getting caught up with them, asking if they were studying hard at school, saying their rosary every day, and obeying their teachers, things I was certain Hugo had never done himself a child.

They nodded and chatted with him and then, each with a plateful of snacks, headed into the den, giggling.

Franck poured himself and the men *kirs*. I stuck to water of course. Rapidly the men plunged into the throes of planning how they were going to begin work on the cellar the very next day, starting with an excavation of the coal and garbage. After that they needed to dig down to give the cellar more ceiling height, hopefully without hitting the cellar that was surely beneath it.

The Romans built the first wine cellars in Beaune. Five centuries later, in the 1100s, the monks of the Cîteaux Abbey began replanting vineyards in the region. A new generation of cellars was built over the old, and so it went until Beaune's underground resembled a honeycomb of cellars.

"We'll have to handle the digging like a young bride on her wedding night," said Robert, using an expression I had definitely never heard before. "Slow and gentle."

I stifled a giggle, but Hugo nodded his broad head fervently. "We don't want to go crashing through the ceiling of the cellar beneath."

"Will you have enough time to work on both the cellar and our house in Villers?" I asked.

We'd hired Hugo, who we had gotten to know when he

worked with us during our renovation of our rental cottage in Villers-la-Faye, to work on the renovations at our house while we stayed at the apartment. His role in renovating our house was key: he needed to punch through a supporting wall between the kitchen and the main living area and install a thick plinth so the entire house didn't fall down. As well, he needed to pour a new concrete veranda. None of these were negligible tasks.

Franck was generally an excellent project manager, but he tended to get distracted with enthusiasm about side projects like the cellar. I knew the cellar was enticing enough to do that and that Hugo would not think twice about following his lead. But at the same time the three men seemed to be swept away on such a powerful tide of momentum that I hated to be the person to pump the brakes. *At least Hugo's suspended prison sentence hasn't come up yet. Small mercies.*

Just as I was beginning to think we were home free, Franck began to wonder out loud how they would be able to park a truck in the middle of the street to load it with excavated materials without causing problems with Beaune's *gendarmes*.

"I'll let you handle that." Hugo laughed. "I'm already on their blacklist."

Robert's dark eyes sharpened. "What do you mean?"

Oh no.

I tried to catch Hugo's eye to shake my head at him, but he was blissfully unaware of any potential problem.

He laughed heartily. "Nothing terrible. It's just that I tried to run over a *gendarme*, so I have a suspended prison sentence. I suppose I have to behave for a while, which is a bore."

"You did what!?" The suppressed anger in Robert's voice made Franck's and Hugo's eyes widen like saucers. I knew for certain at that moment Franck wasn't aware of Robert's *gendarme* past.

"What's the big deal?" Hugo shrugged. "I was just trying to scare him." His round cheeks flushed bright pink. "He got embarrassed, so he reported me."

"I was a *gendarme* for years before retiring form the force," Robert informed Hugo. His expression was thunderous, his brown eyes almost black, and all at once it was the easiest thing in the world to imagine him in a *gendarme* uniform.

Franck's mouth dropped open, and a surprised *"Merde alors"* popped out. Luckily, Hugo's and Robert's gazes were locked, and nobody was paying attention to Franck.

Hugo pushed his chair back. "I had good reason."

"What could possibly be a good enough reason to disrespect the law?" Robert demanded.

"It has to do with that particular *gendarme* trying to prevent me from restoring my house, a sort of mini-château that had fallen into ruin."

Robert didn't say anything, but his eyes softened the tiniest bit. Without knowing it, Hugo had hit on perhaps the only reason that could have any sway with Robert. If there was one thing Robert respected more than law and order, it was restoring France's old buildings.

"This *gendarme* wanted to buy the house... Like I said, it's more of a little château really," Hugo went on, his already ruddy face now crimson. "Very old and much neglected. I knew he wanted to knock it down and subdivide the lot for new construction."

Robert gasped.

This might be okay, I thought.

"It was a complete ruin. I mean, we're talking holes in the floors and ceilings, half the windows broken or punched out of their frames. Nobody wanted to take it on, so the *gendarme* had every reason to think his purchase of the property was as good as done. The village wanted to save it of course, and the property wasn't legally subdividable under the bylaws, but he'd managed to bribe everyone on the village council to give him planning permission to tear it down once he bought it."

"Gives a bad name to all *gendarmes*," Robert muttered. "Dishonorable."

Hugo nodded. "He had no respect for French heritage. As you can imagine, I couldn't have that. This place had the most elegant bones and a roof with the original varnished Flemish tiles...a diamond in the rough. I want to restore it, and I knew my friends and I had the skill to bring it back to life."

I peered closely at Hugo's face. He was blinking back tears.

"And?" Robert demanded.

"I quickly and quietly bought it from the sellers without anyone suspecting I was even interested."

Robert tipped his chin. "So, this *gendarme* wasn't happy?"

"Furious." Hugo gave a smile, as though entertained by his memories. "Worse, he couldn't get back the money he'd used to pay off the councilors. To do that he'd have to admit what he'd done, and he'd lose his post."

"But I still don't see why you had to run over him," Robert said.

"That's because I haven't finished yet," Hugo said. "Instead of admitting defeat, the *gendarme* started to torture me. He vandalized the work site, stole materials, harassed my friends who were helping me, asked for endless paperwork and approvals. He tried to make it impossible for me to do the renovations so I would give up and sell the house to him for next to nothing." Hugo shrugged again. "He left me no choice."

Robert slowly nodded. "You had to send him a message."

"It was the only way to save the restoration project."

Silence fell around the table as we waited for Robert's verdict.

"I would never justify violence against a police officer," Robert began.

I stiffened.

"*Except* in a situation like that," he continued. "France's heritage must be preserved at all cost. It's the highest calling. Besides, corrupt *gendarmes* who abuse their power are scum and defile the job."

"My sentiments exactly," Hugo said.

Franck and I let out sighs of relief.

I went to sleep that night far later than planned but with the satisfaction that at least our cellar team was cemented. Hopefully nobody had other skeletons in their closets...and hopefully there were none in the cellar either.

chapter eight

For the next few days I was posted on the sidewalk of the rue Rousseau Deslandes to block cars during the cellar excavation.

The men had gotten rid of the garbage and coal in the first day—that was the easy part. Now Robert, Hugo, and Franck were taking pickaxes and shovels to the dirt on the cellar floor. They had to haul it all up and into the back of Hugo's truck to take it wherever dirt was hauled. I wasn't interested enough to ask where that was.

As it turned out, the men quickly discovered that my expanded size made me an ideal person to stop traffic. The French were aggressive drivers, but pregnant women were sacrosanct. We had our own parking spots right by the entrance of every shop and our own designated checkout line at the grocery store. Everyone offered us seats and extra food and even Champagne—because the French always said, "Champagne makes beautiful babies." I offended scores of people by turning it down.

The problem was I hated stopping traffic. My innate Canadian politeness hadn't been so far corrupted that I could brazenly hold up people for ten minutes or more and not feel bad about it. Also, it was November, and the winter cold had settled in. My usual winter coat didn't close around my middle anymore. The toggles just couldn't hook up over the swell of the baby.

The idea was to dig out thirty centimeters from the cellar floor, an amount reached by some obscure but precise method of Robert's.

Hugo had brought a few of his workers from our house in

Villers to speed things along. Franck kept assuring me the work in Villers-la-Faye was still being done and that he had posted Luc there as the de facto project manager, but his reassurances were made with the same nonchalance he used when he told me he'd arrive at the girls' school to pick them up on time. He was always late.

I was acutely aware that this baby was coming into the world in January, and we needed to be able to live in our house in Villers by then. Guests had already booked the apartment, so staying longer in Beaune wasn't an option.

So it was with mixed feelings and numb fingers that I stood in the road and blocked cars to allow for another shipment of dirt to be loaded and taken away.

I found myself regretting that in France the whole idea of travel cups was completely foreign. A French person sat down to drink a *café*; one did not stroll around quaffing the stuff from large insulated mugs. That was a crying shame, as I could have so used a hot coffee right then. As soon as Franck returned from unloading the dirt, I was going upstairs for a while to warm up, excavation be damned.

A while later, the truck swung into the rue Rousseau Deslandes again. I gestured at Franck to open his window.

"I'm freezing," I informed him. "I'm going up to the apartment."

"Of course," Franck said. "I'll be up in a moment." He blew me a kiss.

Once upstairs I sat on one of the cast-iron radiators for several minutes, jamming my hands between the metal ridges to thaw them. I sighed as the warmth soaked through my bones.

Franck didn't come up right away, as promised. I was certain he couldn't resist the siren's call of the cellar and had gone down to get an update from the workers.

He'd lost track of time, as usual. Franck had what I termed "time dyslexia." I could never decide whether he truly didn't perceive the passage of time like most people or just didn't care.

When he did come up forty minutes later, I was in the kitchen making a huge mug of milky, sugary tea.

He was quite a sight. He was breathing hard, his hair stuck straight up with sweat, and he was covered from head to toe in limestone-scented dirt.

"What happened to you?"

"Hugo's workers said they couldn't dig any deeper down than seventeen centimeters because they are hitting rock after that."

"And?" I knew Franck wouldn't have accepted this.

"Just as I was arguing with them about it, Robert came over to check on things. He listened to their complaints and, without saying a word, went back across the street and brought two pickaxes. He and I began pickaxing the ground, and we got through just fine. We proved to them it can be done, that it *will* be done with or without them."

"What about treating the job like a young bride on her wedding night?" I asked. This colorful expression had quite captured my fancy. "What if that rock you're pickaxing is the ceiling of the cellar beneath?"

Franck waved his hand. "Robert said it was fine. He said the ceiling of the next cellar would be at least half a meter down. We shamed Hugo's guys soundly enough that they got their own pickaxes from the truck, and we all started pickaxing. We'll get thirty centimeters in the end. Mark my words."

"What are you doing here then?" I asked. I knew that Franck, unlike most people, considered pickaxing to be first-class fun.

"Do you mind coming out one more time? We've filled almost another truck. Can you believe it?"

The shine in Franck's eyes was unmistakable. He was enjoying himself. It was hard to resist.

"Okay, but I need to drink this tea first."

"Deal."

I went back down with my gargantuan belly and blocked more traffic on the rue Rousseau Deslandes under the gunmetal sky.

The drivers looked impatient, but once they saw I was pregnant, they beckoned me to their windows to ask when my baby was due and whether it was a boy or girl.

Once the truck had gone off and the cars could go through again, Franck urged me to accompany him into the cellar. We had to shuffle down two large wooden planks they had placed over the stairs to push and drag out the loads of dirt. I made Franck go in front of me and held on to his sides to avoid slipping forward on top of the baby.

Shovels and pickaxes were propped against the walls and the central pillar, and several buckets sat on the floor. Plastic bins to heap the dirt in and move it up the planks were piled by the foot of the pillar.

Under the blinding light of Luc's bulb, the cellar was beginning to take shape. The ceilings and walls were still a grimy black, but the increased space between the floor and ceiling highlighted the sublime arching lines of the vaults. It was amazing what a difference it made.

"What do you think?" Franck asked, wrapping his arms around me from behind.

"Amazing." I hadn't been down in at least a week, and the change was all the more impressive.

"I know, right?" His voice was full of satisfaction.

"It's going to be stunning."

"I know." His hand snuck under my sweater to touch my bare skin. I shivered, and the baby gave him a kick. "Just like our other production. But you're the one doing all the work for this one. I guess that's why I'm throwing myself into the cellar so much—to not feel useless."

We had been skirmishing about the amount of time he was spending in the cellar, but this explanation made sense.

"This will be a good place to put wine down for the baby," I said.

"I've already preordered several Magnums from Claire." Franck kissed my neck.

I guessed we all prepared in our own way.

chapter nine

Our house in Villers-la-Faye would be ready in two weeks, or at least that's what Franck and Luc had promised me. As the work progressed, I got in the habit of going there with Franck almost every morning after dropping off the girls. Now that the cellar was excavated the required thirty centimeters Robert had decreed, my pregnant self was no longer required for traffic control.

La Maison des Chaumes still looked like a nuclear bomb site, but I had learned from renovating our rental cottage in Villers and our rental house in Magny-les-Villers that things generally looked like that until the last three days, when everything magically came together. The hole between the kitchen and living room still looked like a rough gash in the wall, but it was going to be dry-walled over, and it let an incredible amount of light into the previously enclosed kitchen.

"It makes such a difference," Luc said beside me as he observed the kitchen. As usual, his narrow face and wiry body were covered in a fine layer of drywall dust.

"Bright is always good," I agreed.

"What do you think of the cabinets?"

We turned to examine the brand-new kitchen cabinets made from beautiful pale French oak. So far the counters, sinks, and taps were nowhere to be seen, but the cabinets... The cabinets were great.

"Perfect," I said.

"Durable, too." Luc nodded approving, his brown eyes crinkling in that friendly way of his through his drywall mask. "If there is one area of the house to splurge on, it's the kitchen."

"Are things going okay here without Franck? Be honest."

Luc shrugged. "Maybe not as fast as they would if he were here. He has a way of galvanizing people, as you know."

I chuckled. Franck's method of working alongside tradesmen, only faster and harder, was highly effective.

"But on the whole things are good. Anyway, I'm grateful for the experience of managing the project. I've been playing around with the idea of project management as in addition to electrical and drywall."

I turned to him. "You would be amazing at that. Truly."

He smiled his shy smile. "*Merci.*"

"It's the truth. You're a natural."

Luc's face went bright red. "How are you enjoying Beaune?" he asked in a blatant attempt to change the subject.

As much as I had grown to appreciate the tranquility and lumbering pace of Villers-la-Faye, I was enjoying being in the center of a larger town. I took the girls to the market every Saturday, and I loved walking just a few feet to our favorite boulangerie.

"I'm from a city of several thousand, so Villers-la-Faye was quite an adjustment. Beaune feels...easier."

"Why didn't you buy a house down there?"

I shrugged. "Too expensive, plus Franck wouldn't hear of it."

He grinned. "Yes, we men from the Hautes-Côtes are all the same. I wouldn't consider it either." Luc was from the neighboring village of Meuilley. "It's living up here in the hills or nothing."

"Exactly. So how soon do you think we'll be able to move back?"

"Two weeks," Luc said. "Is that okay?"

"As long as we're in a few days before Christmas." I always took my job of making Christmas magical for the girls seriously, and I needed time to decorate the tree, wrap the presents, and set the scene.

"You will be," Luc promised.

In the end we were able to move out of the Beaune apartment and back to our newly renovated abode in Villers only two days before Christmas. It was a scramble to move in and get everything ready for Christmas morning, and Franck and I stayed up late to wrap a massive Playmobil barn and dig through the basement to find Christmas ornaments.

I was a little ticked that Robert and Franck were determined to work in the cellar even Christmas Eve day. They spent almost every hour down there, rubbing their chins and figuring out the best way to install the wine racks. They were jumping ahead of themselves, of course, but Robert was an inveterate planner.

With me hugely pregnant, and drywall dust still falling three seconds after cleaning it, Christmas that year was a bit of a makeshift affair, but I was proud of myself for pulling it off at all.

Luckily, Franck's sister Stéphanie had us over for her usual Burgundian Christmas lunch, which that year included two roasted geese with chestnut stuffing and an unctuous blackcurrant mousse for dessert. As usual, it began at eleven thirty in the morning, and we got home to La Maison des Chaumes about ten o'clock at night. That year I had to forgo the usual parade of sublime Hospice de Beaune wines that went with each course, but with the baby doing somersaults in my belly, I didn't mind.

Once Christmas was behind us and the girls went back to school, it hit me that it was now January, the month of my due date. I needed to start buying diapers and planning a nursery.

That weekend I managed to pry Franck out of the cellar, mainly because Robert had taken one of his rare trips to his home in Brittany. I declared our weekend project was the baby's nursery.

We didn't have a bedroom for our new baby. As it was, Charlotte and Camille already shared a room.

Franck and I had to carve out a makeshift corner of the office by buying a folding screen that blocked off our desks and computers from the baby's area. Behind it we set up the crib that had been languishing in the stone barn across from Franck's parents' house and an antique dresser I had found and transformed into a changing table.

Yet even with all this done, I still didn't feel ready.

I mentioned this at Sunday lunch at Franck's parents' house.

His aunt Renée waved her hand and pooh-poohed us. "Everyone having babies now is making a great fuss out of nothing," she said. "You get so stressed about having all this *equipment,* but all three of my children spent the first few months of their lives sleeping in a drawer. Trust me, a drawer is all you need. Everything else is just spoiling them."

I was about to laugh when I realized she wasn't joking.

Michèle, Franck's mother, pointed at me with her fork. "That's true. Franck slept in a drawer for the first two months of his life."

Franck looked up. "I did?"

"Of course! What did you think, you had a gilded bed? We were living in a tiny apartment with a leaky roof, and the drawer was one of the only areas of the apartment that was dry."

Franck's eyes went round.

"I put blankets in the drawer for you to sleep on," Michèle added.

As shocking as this sounded, I started to feel significantly better about my perceived lack of preparation. "Well, we do have a crib," I admitted.

Renée waved her hand again. "A crib already? Stop worrying then! Pass me some of those *flageolets* instead."

chapter ten

Subsequent to the revelation about starting life in a drawer, Franck seemed to feel as though by setting up the crib he had acquitted himself of any further baby prep.

One morning in January, Robert phoned Franck while we were finishing breakfast. I was rushing the girls along because I needed to get dressed to go to Beaune with Franck to drop them off at school.

Camille was in tears because I had put the Poulain chocolate powder in her breakfast bowl before pouring in the warm milk.

"I don't get to stir it in!" she wailed, her bottom lip stuck out in protest.

"You got mad at me yesterday because I put the milk in before the powder," I said, exasperated.

"You always do it *wrong*," she threw at me.

"Then don't drink it," I said in a warning tone. "Go and get your cartable ready. *Now.*"

She stalked off. Neither Camille nor I were morning people, and as a result some sort of skirmish erupted most mornings.

I leaned against the counter and sighed. My bones ached with fatigue. Would I ever feel energetic again?

Franck bounded into the kitchen just as I was rinsing the *café au lait* bowls.

"Exciting news! Robert borrowed two power washers from a friend, so we can start power-washing the cellar today!"

I turned around to look at him, incredulous. "We have the preadmission appointment at the hospital at ten o'clock. I reminded you ten minutes ago."

"Didn't you wonder why I was planning on coming to Beaune with you?"

"Um…no." I could see a question forming in his eyes.

I shook my head to ward it off at the pass. "You're coming. The hospital needs us both there. *I* need you there, Franck."

His face fell. "I guess we can start the power-washing after the appointment." He sighed.

He didn't have to act so disappointed. My third trimester hormones and a lack of sleep mixed into a vicious cocktail of resentment, and I took out my anger by scrubbing the kitchen counter with unusual violence.

We made it to the hospital on time, mainly because I barred Franck from checking on the cellar and convinced him to go for a coffee with me at the Brasserie Carnot instead.

We were ushered into the office of the head of obstetrics at the Beaune maternity ward with the formality that attended every medical appointment in France.

I felt lucky to be giving birth at Beaune. It was a mind-bogglingly well-funded hospital because of the massive wine auction every year. The money raised there funded its operations and then some. I'd also heard rumors of hospital dinners coming with glasses of local *premier cru* wines from the hospital's vast stocks.

I was uncertain if that was merely an urban legend in Burgundy, but I was eager to find out.

After the customary introduction and handshakes, we sat down behind the desk. The smell of antiseptic in the hallway luckily didn't penetrate in here. My queasiness from the first trimester had returned a few weeks before, and the smell of hospitals stressed me out at the best of times.

I gave myself a stern mental reminder to use the more formal *vous* as required when dealing with doctors. It didn't come naturally to me, and I'd already offended my traditional French obstetrician with the social solecism of addressing him with the informal *tu*.

"So what date have you and your obstetrician decided on for

the cesarean?" the head of obstetrics asked. He looked the part with neatly clipped gray hair and round wire spectacles.

"January twenty-seventh," I said. The date was lodged in my heart, and it was only six days away. "That will give you enough time to power-wash," I muttered to Franck, a bite in my voice.

"Yes, it will," Franck answered with an arch look.

"What?" The doctor lowered his glasses to better peer at us.

I shook my head. "Nothing."

His forehead wrinkled, but he looked down at the agenda he had open in front of him. He kept flipping one page back and forth, studying the entries.

"Is there a problem?" Franck asked at last.

"Well...*oui*. We've just received a strike notice this morning. All the nurses are planning to strike on January twenty-fourth. We'll need at least four operating-room nurses for your procedure, as well as the recovery room nurses on the ward."

Effing France. This was so typical. After living in France for several years, I paid scant attention to the constant stream of strikes that were a background to French life. I never imagined, however, that a strike would impact my delivery.

"They'll be done striking by the twenty-seventh, *n'est-ce pas?*" I said.

The doctor shrugged. "Impossible to say. Sometimes it's just a day or two. Other times it lasts weeks, months even."

"I have to get this baby out of me!" My voice was replete with the panic of the ninth month. I felt like this child had been gestating in me forever and that I would never not be pregnant.

"How do you feel about January twenty-third as a birthday for your baby?" the doctor asked.

"The twenty-third... But that's in two days!"

"There are no ORs available after that, and the closer your delivery date is to the strike, the higher the chances of your cesarean being cancelled."

"What happens if they cancel my C-section here in Beaune?" Terror was seeping into my voice.

He shrugged. "You'll be sent to give birth in Dijon, or maybe Chalon." I wanted my baby to be born here, at this small hospital at the foot of the Beaune vineyards, not in some massive medical center in the industrial outskirts of Dijon.

I shook my head, still in shock. *I should have expected this.* We found out a few days before Charlotte's due date that she was footling breech. Camille got stuck over one of my hipbones and didn't budge until a cesarean was decided on.

"So the twenty-third will work?" My voice came out thin and strained. "It would be early enough to avoid the strike?"

He nodded. "Definitely."

Franck reached across and patted my hand. "It will be fine."

"Will it?" I said, my eyes darting wildly "Two days from now? *Vraiment?*"

"Yes," he said bracingly. "You'll have the baby, and he or she will quickly become part of our lives, just like Charlotte and Camille."

Easy for him to say. He wasn't having his abdomen sliced open and a human removed in less than forty-eight hours.

"I guess. It doesn't sound like we have any other option," I muttered.

"We'll get you checked in on the night of the twenty-second." The doctor scribbled something in his agenda.

"That's tomorrow," I said, more to myself than anything.

He consulted his agenda again, and his spectacles slipped down his nose. The OR schedule seemed to be entirely handwritten in this man's diary.

"*Oui*, I suppose it is, Madame Germain. You'll be meeting your baby soon. Isn't that enchanting?"

Somehow "enchanted" did not describe how I felt. When Charlotte and Camille were born in Canada, I had checked in the morning of their births.

"How does Franck go about being in the OR with me?" I asked.

The head of obstetrics let out a puff of disbelief and examined Franck. "Surely you don't *actually* want to be there."

"Actually, I do," Franck said. "It won't be the first time. I was there for our two older daughters."

"But there's blood... It's extremely distasteful."

I widened my eyes in disbelief. "Distasteful?"

"Well, for men, yes. Women don't seem to mind as much."

"In Canada it's the norm," I said.

"Well," the doctor huffed. "That's an extremely odd way to conduct a birth, to be sure. It doesn't make me think much of your medical system. Besides, here in Beaune it is strictly against the rules. The nurses can't have fainting husbands on their hands, after all."

"I've never fainted," Franck said. "And I've never vomited. Not even close."

The doctor waved his hand. "I suppose you can ask the nurses, if you're so set on it—though I cannot conceive why. My presence at the births of my five children would not have benefited anybody, least of all me."

The idea of facing down this third C-section without Franck's hand to hold made my breath come in staccato bursts. I needed to change this conversation, *tout de suite*.

"Is it necessary to check in the night before?" I asked.

"Of course," he said.

"Why?"

"We need to prep you for surgery and put on your compression stockings and such."

Pressure stockings? I'd never had to wear pressure stockings before, but I refrained from asking for further details as I was already freaked out.

"All right," I agreed. "What time should I report here tomorrow?"

"Six o'clock," he said. "January twenty-third is a good day to be born," he ended bracingly before ushering us out of his office.

I wasn't sure about that, but one thing was certain: my third child's birth date could not be more French. After all, it was decided by a strike.

chapter eleven

At the hospital's main office, we signed a massive wad of paperwork because this was France, then Franck and I headed out to the parking lot.

I glanced up at the leaden sky. The cold nipped at my face and the circle of sweater-covered belly that protruded from my duffle coat. My nose tingled. It smelled like snow.

"I'm so overwhelmed," I confessed to Franck. "I can't imagine you not being there."

He wrapped his arm around me and pulled me close. "Me neither. I'll move heaven and earth to get myself into that OR."

Even though I could never trust my husband to be on time, I knew instinctively I could trust him on this.

"Remind yourself when you get stressed that we'll meet our baby the day after tomorrow," he added.

Of course I was excited about that, but my feelings were so much more: fear and anticipation, stress and joy... Everything tangled in a knot in my mind.

Was it really so simple for him? As the one who got pregnant and gave birth, it was impossible to imagine myself in Franck's shoes. *What would it be like not to have the pregnancy happen in my body?*

He opened the car door for me. "I'll drop you off in Villers so you can rest, and I'll go and power-wash at the cellar with Robert until I pick up the girls. You can pack your bag for the hospital in peace."

I had been about to climb into my seat, but instead I turned back to him, my eyes narrowed. "How can you think of power-washing at a time like this?"

"Why not?" His eyes were round with surprise.

"Because our baby is arriving the day after tomorrow."

"But the crib is set up, and we have diapers and formula... What else is there to do?"

I was at a loss. It was true that physically, besides packing my suitcase, there wasn't much more, not until the baby arrived anyway. "We need to *mentally* prepare."

He laughed and gave me a peck on the forehead. "Laura, we've already been through this twice. How can we truly prepare for a child's birth? We didn't feel prepared for Charlotte or Camille, and we managed. Face it, *amour*, we're as prepared as we're ever going to be."

I was torn between annoyance and relief. He was right. It did make me feel a bit better to remember we hadn't been any better equipped in our minds or house for Charlotte's or Camille's arrival. Still, it was mind-boggling that he wanted to power-wash at such a juncture.

"Why power-washing?" I asked. "Why now?"

"Who knows how long we can borrow the machines for? We have to use them while we can."

I examined his familiar face. That couldn't be it.

He bowed his head. "Look, I don't feel there's much I can do right now, and it's stressing me out. Cleaning the cellar is something I *can* do that will eventually move that project forward." He placed his hand on my stomach, where our mystery baby gave him a kick. A smile crept over his mouth. "I've already done my part in moving this project forward until the baby arrives, and I will do everything to be right by your side then. I hate not being able to do more right now."

I didn't love it, but it made sense. Maybe it wouldn't be such a bad thing to have a bit of time on my own to pack while Franck was busy with Robert.

"Okay," I said, putting my hand over his. "But keep your phone on in case I go into labor or something."

He nodded. "I will."

"Promise?" Franck was notorious for forgetting his phone in random places and letting his battery go dead.

"*Promis.*"

Clémentine Agathe Germain was born at five minutes after nine on the morning of January twenty-third. We were in an OR that had a full wall made of glass, something I'd never seen before. It looked straight out on the orange winter sun rising over the Beaune vineyards.

It was only after Franck had used all the connections he had via Stéphanie (who, fortuitously for us, worked as a nurse in the ER and was adored by her colleagues) and assured the head nurse and Docteur Le Foulard he had done this twice before without vomiting or fainting that he was gowned up and allowed to stay by my head during the procedure.

The head OR nurse was young and muscular and looked like she wrestled wild boars in her spare time.

"If you faint or get sick in here," she warned as she led Franck into the OR where I was getting a spinal block, "I'm just going to leave you in your pile of vomit. I don't have time to look after a man when his wife is giving birth. You men are all such babies."

Franck meekly agreed to her conditions but rolled his eyes and grinned at me when she turned away. When Clémentine was born, Franck made history as the first father to attend a C-section in Beaune.

He presented an odd appearance, not only because he was a father in the delivery room (*dis-donc!*) and gowned to within an inch of his life but also because the whites of his eyes were blood red from the tiny particles of centuries-old grime he and Robert had washed from the cellar walls.

The thing was, as he explained apologetically, he and Robert had thrown themselves into the job, but they had forgotten one important piece of equipment: goggles. Apparently Robert's eyes were even worse.

Still, even though Franck looked like a demon recently escaped from the underworld, true to his word he was by my side and didn't faint.

Clémentine was tiny—only five pounds—but she was insanely energetic. The minute Docteur le Foulard passed her to Franck, the nurses (who had indeed not begun their strike yet) all exclaimed that she was the carbon copy of her father.

She did look like a miniature female version of Franck. Born in full view of the Beaune vineyards and clearly a Germain through and through, Clémentine was a true Burgundian baby.

chapter twelve

Work resumed only two weeks after Clémentine was born.

Because of the wonderful French medical system, I stayed the allotted seven days in the hospital post-surgery, bonding with my baby. Regular meals were brought to me as well as coffee and thin salted butter biscuits from Brittany at four o'clock every day for the *goûter*. Sadly, wine wasn't served on the obstetrics ward because, I was told by the nurses, "certain doctors" (said with narrowed eyes) didn't feel it was beneficial for nursing mothers.

Even without wine, my stay at the Beaune hospital felt oddly like a visit to the spa, except for the pesky abdominal incision of course.

It was a good thing I rested with Clémentine, because when I got home to Villers, it didn't take long for the wine cellar to become the focus again.

Luckily, Clémentine was an easy baby those first few weeks. Once in Villers I stayed with her while Franck did the school runs and came home for lunch every day. At night she liked sleeping on my stomach in a fetal position, close to my heartbeat, exactly how she must have slept in the womb. She was happy to snooze away most of the day in her little bassinet beside our bed.

Charlotte and Camille were thrilled with their new sister. They had both been unequivocal in their desire for a baby sister, *not* a baby brother. They were old enough at six and eight to watch her in her cuddle seat as I did things in the postpartum period that I never dreamed of with my first and second babies, such as having a shower.

Then the inevitable happened. Charlotte and Camille brought home a nasty winter cold from Saint-Coeur. Certain things were easier with a third baby with older siblings, but virus containment was not one of them.

Clémentine caught the cold immediately. That afternoon when I tried to lay her in her bassinet to sleep, her tiny little nostrils were stuffed up, so instead of settling, she snuffled and cried. I tried laying her on my chest—same thing. Several nights went by in the same fashion and left me so sleep deprived that I had the attention span and brain capacity of a worm.

When Franck brought Charlotte and Camille home from school on the fifth or sixth day of the cold, I passed him Clémentine, who I had been bouncing and rocking in my arms all day as her cold had turned into a rattling cough.

As I was giving the girls their *goûter* in the kitchen of two squares of chocolate in a chunk of baguette, they examined me.

"You look really old today, Maman," Camille finally observed.

"Thank you for that," I muttered.

"Your skin is a strange color," Charlotte added. "Almost gray."

I looked at their rosy cheeks with a certain amount of resentment. "You two are full of compliments."

"Why do you look so terrible?" Camille tilted her little round face, framed by a shiny black bob.

"Because taking care of a sick baby is hard," I said. "And my body has been through a lot, and I am very, very tired."

Charlotte shrugged. "I don't see how it can be that hard."

Franck came in the kitchen just then, which was a good thing as I was close to launching into a rant about the unrecognized work of motherhood. I shooed the girls to their bedroom to continue an elaborate make-believe game involving orphans stranded in Paris.

Franck and I went to the living room, where I collapsed on the couch, grabbed the nearest pillow, and covered my face with it. On days like this one, motherhood tested my deepest reserve of patience. My gas tank was empty. I had nothing left.

Clem quickly stopped fussing in Franck's arms. "Look!" he said. "She's calming down."

I made a wordless noise that summed up the frustration roiling in me, but Franck remained unfazed.

"You won't believe the idea Robert had today," he continued.

I was too tired to ask what it was, but I could tell from his enthusiasm that he was going to tell me regardless.

"Flowerpots."

I lowered the cushion from my face, wondering if I had heard correctly. "What?"

The cellar was…well, a cellar. There was no natural light besides that from the street if the door was open. It was hardly an ideal place to grow flowers.

"Flowerpots," he repeated.

I did not feel up to the task of penetrating this mystery further, so I merely raised my eyebrows.

"For the tasting table."

"What tasting table?"

Franck waved his fingers in front of Clémentine's body, which he had tucked closely against his chest with one arm. "I may not have mentioned it. Robert and I have been discussing the need for a tasting table for a while now. We can't use the cellar for proper wine tastings if we don't have a tasting table, can we?"

"What's wrong with an overturned barrel?" In most of our friends' cellars in Burgundy, winemakers or not, old barrels served as perfectly adequate tasting tables.

Franck waved his fingers again, and I saw Clem had fallen asleep against him. "Robert believes barrels are a copout. He thinks the cellar needs a tasting table with *presence*."

"We have a twenty-one-day-old baby with a cold," I reminded him. "We should be copping out every chance we get."

"Don't worry, Robert has done half a dozen of these before.

It's going to be gorgeous."

"And how much is this 'presence' going to cost us?" I didn't love being the wet blanket who always reminded Franck of our smaller-than-a-shoestring budget, but he did have a tendency to get carried away.

He shook his head. "Not expensive. That's where the flower-pots come in. Robert is a genius!"

The idea, as Franck needed no encouragement to explain, was to stack two flowerpots filled with concrete one on top of the other and use them as a base for the tasting table.

"Hugo was working with us today, and he thinks it's brilliant, too."

"How's Hugo?" I realized how cut off I felt from the non-baby world. "Has he tried to run down any more *gendarmes* recently?"

Franck smiled and shook his head. "No, he's being *très sage*...or so he told me. Oh! I almost forgot. He gave me a present for you."

He brought me a present haphazardly wrapped with what looked like Christmas paper, and I ripped it open. Inside was the most exquisite pink floral embroidered dress and a matching bonnet. Like most French baby clothes, it was beautifully made with soft, fine cotton.

"This is so beautiful." I smoothed my hand over the dress.

"He told me to tell you he picked it out himself, and Clémentine should be able to wear it when she's six months. The saleslady told him we probably have enough newborn clothes, and they grow out of those so fast anyway."

"I have to thank him in person," I said. I was, yet again, truly touched by the thoughtfulness of our tradesmen. "It's beautiful."

Robert had visited me in the hospital bearing the most massive bouquet of roses I had ever seen as well as a box of Beaune's finest chocolates from Chez Bouché. "For the brave *maman*." He had passed them to me with a wink.

"Hugo will be at the cellar the day after tomorrow," Franck said. "And the flowerpots should be installed by then, too. Do you and Clémentine feel up to a little outing?" He eyed me. "I think it might be good for you to get out of the house for a bit."

"Yes," I said. "I clearly need to see these flowerpots in person and thank Hugo. Anyway, it'll be good for me to go out."

Two days later, when we'd dropped the girls at school after lunch, Franck and I brought Clémentine to Beaune for her first ever visit to the wine cellar… Well, her first visit ex utero, in any case.

Hugo and Robert were waiting for us on the sidewalk, and I gushed thanks about the dress to Hugo until it became clear from his bright-red face and darting blue eyes I was embarrassing him with my effusiveness.

Robert and Hugo took turns holding Clémentine and were full of admiration for how she already had a strong neck and a solid grip with her tiny fingers.

"She has such strong hands," Hugo marveled. "She might become a fine stonemason one day." It was such a juxtaposition seeing this burly man hold a tiny baby, but he did it with no trace of awkwardness. "She's the spitting image of her father," he said as he handed her back.

It was true. Her olive complexion, dark, almond-shaped eyes, and full mouth were all Franck.

"I know. Can you believe the irony?" I said. "I was the one who pushed for a third, and here she is, a carbon copy of her father."

Robert and Hugo laughed and beckoned us into the cellar.

Franck held Clémentine close to his chest as we descended the stairs. When we were safely at the bottom, I noticed something covered by a muddy tarp in the back of the cellar. Had Robert orchestrated a dramatic reveal?

The cellar was no longer lit with Luc's powerful light. Franck had told me while I was in the hospital that it had been smashed by a misdirected spray from the power washer and replaced with a dim work light hung from a metal hook that protruded from the stone pillar. Who knew why that had been installed hundreds of years before.

"So, this tasting table?" I nodded to the mystery object. "Is that it?"

"*Oui, oui, oui,*" said Robert, rubbing his hands together and waggling his thick black eyebrows. "I covered it with the tarp so the concrete could dry without any animals getting stuck in it."

My eyes darted to the dark corners of the cellar. "Animals?"

"You know," Hugo said cheerfully. "Snakes, spiders, rats, and the like. I think we got rid of most of those with the power-washing, but underground one never knows."

I gulped. Clémentine hiccupped.

"Now, you must tell me," he said, walking over to grasp the muddy tarp. He whipped it off with a flourish worthy of a ringmaster. "What do you think?"

I blinked. Franck was right. Robert was a genius. The stacked flowerpots convincingly tricked the eye into seeing two huge cubes of rough-hewn stone. It was exactly the look we had pictured but at a sliver of the price.

"Each flowerpot cost only ten euros," Robert said proudly.

I moved closer and ran my hand over the pots. "Even up close I wouldn't be able to tell this base isn't made of real stone."

"I know," Robert said, nodding and smiling.

"Was it hard to do?"

"Not difficult so much as delicate getting everything to line up properly and filling the pots with concrete without cracking them open," Robert said. "Had to be handled like a bride on her wedding night."

"Ah!" I said, biting my lip to keep from laughing. "Right."

"What are you thinking for a tabletop?" I asked. My curiosity was caught, and it felt wonderful to be engaged in the normal course of life again. Caught in sick-baby world, I didn't realize how much I'd missed this until now. For the moment we just had a column. It was a fantastic column, but a tasting table it was not. Not yet, anyway.

Robert ticked his finger at me. "Ah, we need to visit the quarry and pick out a slab of real stone. No pretend materials for that.

Don't you agree, Hugo?"

Hugo nodded. It was like he and Robert were now of one mind. "We'll get a nice, substantial one. I'll help pick it out."

chapter thirteen

Three nights later Franck came home the from quarry with his brows drawn. I was relieved to hear the crunch of his tires on the gravel driveway. The February cold had set in, and the winding road from Beaune to Villers-la-Faye was slick with black ice.

"Did you find a slab?" I asked as I supervised Charlotte feeding Clémentine her evening bottle.

"We did." He joined us on the couch. "It's *sublime*."

"Then why do you look so worried?"

"Robert and Hugo lost their hearts to it. It *is* beautiful, and they assured me we'll be able to manage just fine—"

"But?"

Franck rubbed his face with his hands. "But it must weigh five hundred kilograms. It's a beast. How are we going to get it down there and lifted on top of the table? There's only three of us, and you won't be able to help because of your incision." Franck observed me thoughtfully.

"You're right about that." Clémentine was my third cesarean, and the last thing I needed was my stomach splitting open on the rue Rousseau Deslandes. "Surely Robert has a plan." I had never known Robert *not* to have a plan.

Franck shrugged. "That's what worries me. He said we'd figure it out tomorrow morning when we pick it up. I'm not sure he does have a plan."

Franck was generally allergic to planning *anything*, so for him to be concerned, the situation had to be troubling.

The next morning I arranged for my father-in-law to drive Clémentine and me to Beaune to watch this event unfold. We arrived on the rue Rousseau Deslandes before the stonemason's truck containing the beastly stone. Whew. We hadn't missed anything.

"Are you going to stay and watch?" I asked my father-in-law.

"No, ah, I need to get home to Villers," he said, panic in his translucent-blue eyes. "Franck can bring you back, *n'est-ce pas?*"

I nodded. "*Oui,* but aren't you curious to see how they're going to manage this?"

"Laura." Our eyes met. "What are the chances of me watching without being enlisted to help? My knees are in bad shape right now."

"Good point," I said. "I have a C-section incision and a baby, but I guess you'd be fair game."

Franck could pretty much persuade anyone into anything, so I was sympathetic to André's plight. "Leave now while you can," I advised.

"Don't let Franck talk you into lifting anything!" André reminded me over his shoulder just before he lowered himself into his car and gunned the engine. He sped away before I could reassure him I wouldn't.

I didn't have to wait long for the truck to pull up. Franck asked me to stop traffic again. *Merde.* That was stupid of me. I hadn't considered being roped into service that way. I shook my head. "Not with Clémentine in my arms. No way."

His eyes flicked to our baby, then back at me. "I guess you're right," he conceded.

I planned to enjoy my front row seat, free of any threat of being put to work. Hugo hopped out of his truck—a white Traffic that was so dusty it could pass for beige—and opened the back doors. Inside, on a splintered wooden pallet, lay a glorious, monstrous piece of unpolished local marble. This was no flowerpot.

I was dying to ask them what their plan was—how the three of them, strong as they surely were, could even contemplate moving that slab without the help of some heavy machinery. I had noticed the cobblestones were icy in patches, which would add to the dicey nature of the entire endeavor.

There was much grave conversation around the tailgate about which way to attack this Herculean task. A man I'd never seen before drifted around the truck from the opposite sidewalk and joined in. The cellar door of the neighboring Champy winery opened, and a heavyset man with an Eastern European accent wandered over and bent his head to listen earnestly to the conversation. He said something, then returned five minutes later with two extra men and two thick coiled ropes, one around each forearm.

During his short absence, two other men had also been drawn by the siren's call of the stone and quickly began to test the strength of the rope.

I was amazed. They had gone from three to nine men in the matter of fifteen minutes. Was there some sort of male homing frequency I was deaf to? Where had all these men come from? How did they know they were needed?

More muttered planning ensued, then finally Robert clapped his hands over his head. *"Bon alors!"* he declared. *"On attaque!"*

They were going to start, whether they were ready or not, but a shout from above halted everyone before they could begin. "I come help!"

I peered up. The living room windows at our apartment above were flung open, and a blond man's head was sticking out. "I come help you!" he repeated in heavily accented French. I'd forgotten a German couple were renting our apartment for the next two weeks. "I am strong!"

I looked back to the group, not at all sure how this offer would be taken. Even though most of these men weren't alive during the Second World War, the scars from that time ran deep in French families. This was particularly the case in Burgundy, which had been so close to the divide between Occupied and

Unoccupied France. Even Mémé, who swore she believed in reconciliation and working together with the Germans, confessed that she couldn't hear German without it making her throat close with terror.

"That's okay." Franck waved up at him. "I think we should be fine. Thank you, though!"

"My name is Fritz," the man said. "And I come help." He disappeared from the window. Either he hadn't understood Franck's fast French, or he was truly determined to be part of this.

One of the mystery men muttered something I only half heard, but his tone didn't sound diplomatic.

"Now, now." Robert tsked. "It's nice that he wants to help. The Germans could never be faulted for their work ethic, you know."

Fritz burst through the door onto the street, well over six feet of Teutonic muscle. The men examined him with new respect. "What can I do?" He didn't bother asking why we were moving this huge slab of stone.

Robert positioned Fritz on the front side, so he would be walking backward and carrying the most weight. That, I knew, was a mark of trust and a pointed message to the other helpers. The men began to shove the stone out of the truck. It moved bit by bit, but I figured slow was better than haste; if that thing fell, it could shatter a foot and probably the cobblestoned street as well. I prayed no one would slip on black ice.

When there was finally more marble outside the truck bed than in, gravity took hold, and the stone lurched, but Franck, Robert, and Fritz caught and somehow held it. Robert's and Franck's faces were fuchsia, and every vein on their bodies popped out from their skin. Fritz, however, looked completely normal and almost casual about lifting the stone. A grin was plastered on his face, as though he was having the time of his life.

Hugo and the guy from Champy secured the ropes around the stone's bulk.

Shuffling, sweating, panting, and swearing—except for Fritz, who just kept smiling—the ten men managed to move the beast to the top of the wooden planks. These were the same ones they had used to haul up coal, and they now covered half the stairway into the cellar. I hoped those planks were solid.

Just then I realized a fault in their plan. They had no one in the cellar to catch the stone as it slid down the planks.

But my heart skipped a beat as I watched Franck lead Robert, Hugo, and Fritz down the tiny strip of uncovered stairs.

If the man from Champy and his two colleagues weren't able to hang on to the ropes, or worse yet, if the ropes broke, the slab could easy crush one of the men at the bottom, if not two. Franck called up to say they were standing ready.

The man from Champy, whom I was standing only feet from, was by no means a spring chicken. He looked like he came from sturdy Slavic stock, but right now he clutched the rope, his face bright red and slicked with sweat. *He's ripe for a coronary*, I thought. In my mind I quickly flipped through the CPR procedures I had learned in lifeguarding class many years before.

For all I knew, the other men had probably been strolling down the rue Rousseau Deslandes, perhaps counting their *centimes* to buy a baguette at the wonderful boulangerie at the end of the street, when they were pulled in by the magical allure of the stone and the centrifugal force of Franck and Robert's enthusiasm. André had been wise to escape while he had the chance. Their fervor clearly acted like a whirlpool, sucking in innocent bystanders—or in the case of Fritz, eager participants.

Grunts rose from the cellar, but I didn't dare move closer. Under no circumstances did I want to jostle the men holding the ropes. At least there wasn't any screaming...yet.

Finally, I heard Hugo's voice. *"C'est bon!"* It was good; the stone had arrived at the bottom. The ropes slackened, and the Champy man pulled them up. The big man and his two helpers promptly descended into the cellar.

I couldn't go down holding Clémentine with the wooden plank still covering most of the staircase. Instead, I crept closer to hear shouted instructions and watch the forms in the dim light below as the men pulled the stone from the bottom of the plank and moved it farther into the cellar. How do you say "hernia" in French?

A few minutes later I heard Fritz's voice. "*Es ist gut?*"

The men eventually staggered one by one out of the cellar, wiping their brows and rubbing their backs. Fritz, of course, looked as fresh as a daisy. He wasn't even sweating from what I could see. I could tell they were all satisfied by the glow in their eyes.

Franck clapped his hands together as soon as he popped out onto the sidewalk.

"I have wine for all of us downstairs to celebrate," he declared. "But first, the bottom stairstep."

Stairstep?

Luckily Clem was sleeping soundly against my chest, and I was able to watch in wonder as Franck talked his slap-dash team into sliding down the extra stone step, needed after the excavation, that Hugo had picked up at the quarry and hidden behind the tabletop in the back of his van. Maybe it wasn't as heavy as the tabletop, but it was long and awkward in shape…and probably weighed close to three hundred kilos.

I wondered if my husband hadn't invented the phrase "kill two birds with one stone"—or perhaps more aptly "kill two innocent bystanders with one seriously heavy stone step."

I supposed after the larger piece, the stone step felt like child's play, because in a matter of ten minutes, it was at the bottom, and Franck was baptizing the new tabletop by serving the team Chablis Grand Cru. Fritz had more than proved himself and grinned as he was slapped on the back and congratulated for his formidable strength by the rest of the men.

Clémentine didn't stir even when I raised a glass to toast Franco-German cooperation.

chapter **fourteen**

JULY 2008

Since he'd finished the renovations of La Maison des Chaumes, Luc had been busy on another big job in Dijon, so Franck and I had to turn to an unknown electrician for a quote on properly wiring and lighting the cellar.

My parents were over for a visit from Canada when Franck received the emailed quote.

He came into the kitchen, where my mom was cuddling a now six-month-old Clémentine. I thought maybe our baby would begin to look less like Franck as she moved past the newborn stage, but...nope. If anything, the months solidified the resemblance between Clémentine and her *papa*. She had the same almond-shaped hazel eyes, high cheekbones, and full mouth.

"I just got an email from the electrician," Franck said, twisting his mouth into a grimace.

"Oh?" I said, a bit distracted as I sliced a piece of oozy Époisses cheese and spread it on a fresh baguette. Six months out, I was still not quite myself after giving birth. Having three children instead of two felt right, but it did tip the balance of our lives from barely controlled chaos to complete chaos. I was still in the process of surrendering to that.

The girls kept swapping viruses like relay batons throughout the spring, and I was tired as well as frustrated I hadn't yet gotten back to my usual writing and other creative pursuits. I was growing impatient.

Usually after lunch or dinner was the only time of the day we ate cheese in France, but my father, who had long been terrified of stinky French cheese, especially the regional specialty Époisses, which was reliably redolent of dirty old socks, had finally gathered the courage to taste a slice just days before.

As soon as he'd swallowed it, my father underwent the cheese version of a religious conversion.

Because he is an all-or-nothing person (gee, I wonder who I inherited that from?), he rapidly went from fearing Époisses to wanting to eat it all day long.

In bed the night before, Franck and I had calculated than since that first taste six days earlier, my father had consumed on average an entire Époisses round a day, *by himself*. It was no surprise he had started complaining of a touchy stomach.

"Two thousand euros," Franck said. "That's what the electrician quoted."

My knife stilled. "What?" *I must not have heard that correctly.*

"Yeah, I know. Insane, *nest-ce pas?*"

"It's the most ridiculous thing I've ever heard. How can he possibly justify that?"

"He told about how tricky it was to install indirect and atmospheric lighting to highlight the cellar's vaults and pillars, blah, blah, blah."

I groaned. "I wish Luc could do it."

"I know," Franck said. He was as sad as I was about that fact. "But the job in Dijon is a great opportunity for his new business. We like him too much to have him compromise, don't we?"

Franck was right. "No, we can't bother him now." Still, I couldn't help but wish the timing was better.

"What are you talking about?" my mom asked, bobbing up and down with Clémentine in her arms.

It was then I realized Franck and I had been speaking in French. Since moving to France we never spoke English as a family anymore, but I kept forgetting that I needed to translate for my parents.

"It's the electrician's quote," I said. "It's ridiculously high."

"How about that friend of yours across the street?" my dad

suggested. "Robert? Could he help?"

Franck had introduced Robert to my dad on the previous trip, and even though the two men could not speak the same language, they had rapidly formed a mutual admiration society.

My dad appreciated hard workers, and Robert was nothing if not a hard worker. As for Robert, he told us he could tell my father was an old-school "man of his word" like himself.

Sadly, however, Robert had been sidelined since shortly after the tasting table installation due to a bad accident involving a handheld circular grinder.

He had been doing some carpentry at the baron's place when his hand slipped and he sliced open his thigh with his *meuleuse*. Robert had somehow managed to find a filthy rag to wrap a tourniquet around his leg, then he got in his car and drove around the boulevard in Beaune to the ER.

We got the full account of his arrival, as Stéphanie, Franck's sister, happened to be working triage that evening. Robert had half lurched, half crashed through the ER doors, his leg gushing blood through the now-crimson cloth. He'd shouted, *"Meuleuse!"* then fainted on the ER linoleum.

He'd required hundreds of stiches and had been banished (in his opinion it was banishment, as he loved nothing better than his restoration work) to Brittany to stay with his wife. He was officially on sick leave until his leg healed.

He had returned to Beaune only a week before, and he had celebrated his homecoming with Franck and my father in our wine cellar. I'd been called to pick them up. Luckily my mother had kept Clémentine in Villers because getting the three of them out of the cellar was a formidable task.

That night when I had escorted Robert across the street, he'd leaned heavily on my arm, but whether it was from the bad leg or the sheer amount of wine in his belly, I was unsure. "Should you be mixing wine with painkillers?" I'd asked, interrupting his enthusiastic rendition of "Le Ban Bourgignon."

"Most likely not." He'd hiccupped. "Don't tell Nurse Stéphanie, *promis?*"

Stéphanie had told us about the home visits Robert had been

receiving from her colleagues since he returned to Beaune.

They kept reminding him to stay off his leg, but of course he didn't. When the nurse arrived one day, she found him at the top of a ladder chiseling out mortar between the stones in an old wall.

Luckily, he'd begun singing again before I had to give him an answer. I managed to get him safely across the road to the baron's. He swore he would go straight to bed.

Franck and my father had tumbled into the back seat of our car, and they'd sung continuous rounds of "Le Ban Bourgignon" between my father's praises of Robert.

Both Franck and I felt so grateful for the help that Robert had already given us that we felt bad asking him for anything else, especially considering his leg.

"Do you think we should ask him?"

Franck nodded. "I know he must have some thoughts about it, but I *won't* let him help us. His leg is still healing. Stéphanie said his cut went right to the bone."

I made a face. "We can't give him a reason to misbehave." Robert was a bad enough patient on his own; the last thing he needed was encouragement to overextend himself. Still, could it hurt to just ask advice? Robert clearly loved giving it, and he was a source of so many ingenious ideas.

"Just ask," I said. "It couldn't hurt."

The next night Franck and I lay in bed after my parents had returned to La Maison de la Vieille Vigne after dinner.

"So? What did Robert say?" I asked. Franck had gone to visit him that afternoon.

"He's a life saver," Franck said. "Within minutes of me knocking on the baron's door, Robert had a plan. The first step involved going to buy lights at Bricorama in Beaune."

"I hope he didn't come with you."

Franck bit his lip. "He insisted," he finally admitted. "He said

I wouldn't know which lights to buy and that he needed to stretch his leg."

"Stretch his leg?" I made a sound of disbelief.

"I warned him not to forget it was my sister who treated him and that I knew very well he was supposed to stay off his leg, not stretch it."

"And?"

Franck chuckled in the dark. "Robert waved his hand. 'No need to bother her with this. She's busy enough as it is,' he said. 'I know what's best for me.'"

"So you caved?" I asked. "I get it. He can be very persuasive."

"He asked how I would enjoy being careful all the time like some sort of breakable ornament."

"Ah."

"That was the clincher for me. It's true; I would hate it."

So Robert had led Franck through Bricorama to find the cheapest, most basic outdoor lights on the shelves. Franck recounted their trip.

"Are you sure?" he had asked, feeling doubt when he examined the ugly specimens.

"Positive." Robert had nodded. "Often with renovations, the most basic materials are the best. It's what we do with them that counts." He'd tapped the side of his head. "That's where ingenuity comes in."

Franck had nodded. "But they're not going to be very, you know, attractive if they're exposed."

"Don't you worry about that." Robert had raised his finger. "Do you remember the lights in the baron's cellar? These are going to look just as good."

"Oh, right!" I exclaimed when Franck paused. "They looked so authentic that I just figured they had always been there. He thinks we can do the same thing?"

"Yes."

"He's a miracle worker."

"He is." Franck gave me a final kiss and then rolled over in his sleep position. "But we have to keep in mind that he's an injured miracle worker."

chapter **fifteen**

We had taken to inviting Robert to Villers for dinner. He was all alone at the baron's domaine, not to mention he was invariably fascinating company.

Awkward silence never fell over the dinner table when Robert was there. He would sing, he would laugh, and even though I knew he was a true connoisseur of fine food and wine, he professed to be delighted with anything we put on his plate. That, to me, was the mark of a true gentleman.

We had polished off a beautiful *coq au vin* that Franck had slowly cooked all day as well as homemade purée of potatoes that I had steamed and mashed with generous quantities of cream and butter.

We were on to the cheese platter, and Robert was in the process of cutting off another slice of twenty-month-aged Comté that married perfectly with our second bottle of Claire's Hautes-Côtes de Beaune. My father, meanwhile, was making serious inroads on his second Époisses of the day. It was only then that Robert enlightened us about his plan for lighting the cellar.

"So have you been wondering how we're going to hide those ugly lights?" His right eyebrow quirked up. Robert had the thickest, most expressive eyebrows of anyone I had ever met.

"Like you did in the baron's cellar?"

Robert shot an accusing look at Franck. "You told her?"

Franck winced. "Sorry."

He waved his hand. "No matter. I just like a surprise. In any case, we need to find rocks. Remember the lights on the floor of the baron's cellar? How the light shines up from the slabs of rock?"

I nodded. Before I could ask, he answered my next question. "I've found a source for some perfect local marble we can prop around the lights to aim their beams where we want—up the pillars and such."

The ochre color of the local rock was beautiful, and as Burgundy was once the site of an inland sea many centuries ago, they often contained incredible fossils of prehistoric ferns and bugs as well as nautilus shells.

"But nice stone is not easy to come by—or cheap," I said. "Where?"

Robert tapped the side of his nose, perfectly inhabiting the role of sage.

"A quarry?" I guessed.

There were a number of marble quarries around our area of Burgundy, besides the one where Franck and Robert had found the tabletop and bottom step. It was a little-known fact that the marble used at Charles de Gaulle and JFK airports came direct from quarries in Burgundy.

Robert shook his head, his mouth pursed. "No."

"Where then?" Franck asked.

"I have a friend." He was enjoying this.

Robert had made a few other local friends besides Franck, and they all seemed to be secret sources of covert things.

"My friend has been keeping tabs on a certain field," Robert continued, waving his knife to add extra flourish. "He was driving in the *arrière-côtes* one day and saw this unkempt field that looked abandoned. In the middle was a pile of local stones— lovely ones. Perhaps there was a *cabotte* or something on the land that fell down."

Cabottes were little stone huts that dotted the vineyards around the Côte D'Or and were traditionally used by winemakers to store tools or take shelter from the thunderstorms that rolled through the area.

"An abandoned field?" Franck said. "That's odd." The land in Burgundy was so valuable for its winemaking potential that abandoned land was not something one came across very often. Some fields were purposely left to go fallow for a year or two, but those didn't look abandoned.

"I know," Robert said. "I thought the same thing, but it's probably caught up in some inheritance dispute."

That was a plausible explanation. The combination of the extortionate French inheritance taxes and the complexity of passing down wine holdings from one generation to the next meant the occasional piece of property was held for years in estate law purgatory.

"In any case, the field is not looked after," Robert concluded. "I propose we go and make our selection of rocks there."

Burgundians were extremely territorial, and I had no desire to come face to face with a Burgundian toting a shotgun if we trespassed on a field. "Is that legal?" I asked.

Franck shot me a sharp look of reproach, as though I was insulting Robert to ask such a thing.

"I think we would be doing them a favor by helping them clear some of those rocks." Robert was skirting my question. "It's a terrible shame to see land just sitting there, underused and unkept."

Ah, I understood now. Just like his acceptance of Hugo's crime, the abandoned field fell in the category of moral laws that lay above legal laws for Robert. I could well believe that such negligence perturbed him down to his organized, meticulous soul.

My dad asked what we were talking about, and I quickly translated the gist of the conversation and my question.

"Don't forget I was a *gendarme*," Robert assured us. "I know the difference between right and wrong."

Perhaps it was a copout, but I was happy to have the burden of moral judgment tidily removed from my hands.

"Someone who can't take care of their things doesn't really deserve to possess them," Franck added.

"*Exactement*," Robert agreed, emphatic.

I translated this for Dad, who was nodding at me, indicating with his finger that I hurry with the translation.

Now, my father's rule of thumb for life—one that he declared on a regular basis—was to never engage in any activity he wouldn't be happy to have splashed across the front page of the local newspaper. Besides a spree to Tijuana in his parents' Buick in the 1950s shortly after he got his driving license, my father was one of the most law-abiding people I knew.

I waited for him to digest the translation I'd just provided, unsure what he would think of Robert's proposition, ex-*gendarme* or not.

"When can we go?" my dad asked, his eyes bright with the enthusiasm of an eight-year-old boy.

I laughed. People never stopped surprising me.

Robert must have understood enough English to understand that. "Now." He grinned at my dad's eagerness.

I glanced outside the kitchen window. It was early July, and the sun went down late, but our dinner had started at nine o'clock and proceeded at a lingering Burgundy pace. It was dark outside. Perfect for an undercover operation such as absconding with rocks, but how would we choose rocks in the dark?

"We won't be able to see anything." I pointed out the obvious.

"It's a clear night," Robert said. "And there's a nice full moon in the sky. Besides, doing it at night will avoid a lot of questions. People might not understand why we're rooting around in someone's field if we go during the day, *tu vois*."

Oh, I saw. Robert hadn't just come up with this plan over the cheese platter.

Creeping out in the moonlight reeked of illegal behavior, but it also sounded like a hell of a lot of fun, precisely the kind of fun I'd missed staying at home with Clémentine.

"Let's go," Franck said, his eyes flashing.

"I'm coming."

"You are?" Franck looked at me, surprised.

"Are you kidding?" I said. "I wouldn't miss this for the world. Mom, do you mind watching the girls?"

I could tell from Charlotte's and Camille's voices from their bedroom that they weren't asleep yet, something I didn't worry about at this time of year. School was out, and we were all keeping summer hours. They had completely adapted to a French summer routine, which meant eating dinner anywhere from eight-thirty to ten o'clock and heading to bed around midnight.

She nodded, looking relieved not to be part of our motley expedition. It was so warm out in the evenings I didn't need a sweater over my linen tunic and shorts.

I did, however, go down to the basement and pull on my rubber boots. Who knew what that abandoned field contained? One thing was certain: it was not the time to skimp on sturdy footwear.

I also picked up my winter gloves. Vipers—tiny poisonous snakes—were known to nest in rock piles and walls, especially in the warmth of the summer. Better safe than sorry.

When I got back upstairs, the men were suiting up in the front hallway amid lots of laughter. We all had what the French refer to as "warm ears" after our wine at dinner.

Franck turned to me, but instead of commenting on my odd outfit, he nodded in approval. He shuffled closer and slid his arm across my shoulder. "Your practicality is surprisingly sexy."

I brandished a rubber boot–clad leg. "Fetching, *n'est-ce pas*?"

He squeezed my shoulder, then went to help Robert, who was struggling to bend over and do up his boots. His injured leg had momentarily slipped my mind.

"Maybe you should stay in the car," I said to Robert. "You shouldn't be traipsing around under the moonlight in abandoned fields with your leg like that. Stéphanie will have our heads."

"Stay in the car!" He spat out the words as if they were poison. "Never!"

I glanced at Franck, and he slowly shook his head. Trying to stop Robert would be like trying to stop a wave coming to shore.

chapter sixteen

A minute or two later I found myself in the back seat of our green station wagon driving at Franck's usual breakneck speed along moonlit gravel roads. Robert was right; the sky was cloudless and full of pinpricks of stars.

Robert remembered the approximate direction of the field but not the precise location, so we weaved back and forth on the narrow, interconnecting vineyard roads for at least half an hour, doubling back on our tracks and doing multiple U-turns. Robert kept up a running navigation with his face plastered against the car window.

Just as I began to consider that we might never find the promised field—maybe it had been plowed and planted with vineyards, or cleaned up and the pile of old stones removed, or maybe his friend had simply dreamed it, Robert cried, "That's it!" Franck screeched to a halt.

I peered out the window on my side. The moon shone down on a field that did, indeed, look as unkept as Robert had described. It looked extremely out of place among the cared-for rows of vines and blackcurrants.

I could make out a dark hump near the middle of the field. That had to be the promised stone pile. Given the waist-high weeds that surrounded it, I could see why Robert felt the rocks were fair game.

I began to open my door to get out when Robert jerked around in his seat. "Be careful getting out," he said. "I believe there is a bit of a ditch between the field and the road."

Robert was on the same side of the car as me, in the front passenger seat.

"What about you?" I asked. "How are you going to get out?"

"I'll be fine." Before I could add anything else, he opened the door and stepped out, then disappeared. The only indication he was still there at all was a trail of French expletives.

I quickly shuffled to the driver's side door, and by the time I reached the front, Franck and my dad were helping Robert out of what I could now see was a three-foot-deep ditch between the shoulder of the road and the beginning of the field.

Robert was swearing, but he was standing up with some help from Franck.

"Did you tear the stitches?" I asked, dreading the worst.

"Don't you worry, Laura," he said. "I only stretched them a bit. Be careful you don't fall in the ditch. It's even steeper than I remember."

"It's not me I'm worried about," I muttered in English.

It was truly a miracle that Robert's wife in Brittany hadn't murdered him yet. Maybe there was a very good reason why she seemed content to have him spend long stretches of time away from her.

"How are we going to get across?" my dad asked me in English.

I translated the question for Franck and Robert, and I was extremely curious to hear their answer. The ditch, from my rough estimates, was about four feet wide.

I could see Franck shrug in the moonlight. "Only way is to jump, I guess. If I jump first I can act as an anchor for Robert and, you know, catch him."

I translated for my dad, who frowned. I had been asking myself the same thing. Our eyes met. *Yup.* I gave him a tiny nod of agreement. It did not sound like a well-thought-out plan.

Before I could formulate a reasoned protest, Franck leaped across the ditch. "It's nothing!" he declared from the other side.

"That's what I thought," Robert said brazenly. "I need to test my leg anyway."

He stepped back with a wince and waved at me to go ahead of

him. "Ladies first," he said, gallant even in the most inconvenient situations.

"You can do this, Laura," Franck said.

He knew me well. It had become abundantly clear in our many years together that Franck was a natural athlete; I was not. In high school I was always the last student gasping over the finish line of the school-wide 800-meter run and the one who couldn't make it over even the lowest setting on the high jump.

I couldn't chicken out now, though. As much as Robert had to prove he was still himself even with a slashed leg, I needed to prove to myself that, even with three children, I was still a force to be reckoned with.

I took three steps back until I bumped into the car behind me, in order to give myself a running start. I needed all the help I could get. I just hoped I could figure out when I should take off and go airborne.

I took a deep breath and then ran, launching myself into Franck's arms instead of looking down at the ditch.

My outstretched foot didn't quite make it to the opposite side and slipped down the side of the bank. I felt gravity take hold, but then I was yanked up by Franck. He grabbed my forearms and hauled me beside him on the field.

"See? That wasn't so bad," he said.

I blew out a huff of relief. It hadn't been pretty, and I'd needed help, but I'd made it.

I turned to watch Robert. I was even more worried about his jump than I'd been about mine. I wasn't a coordinated person, but I didn't quite make it with two functioning legs. How was Robert going to manage with one leg that not long ago was almost cleaved in two with a circular grinder?

Unlike me, Robert didn't seem to be suffering from either nerves or hesitation. He didn't even start with a bit of a run like I had. Instead he stretched out his good leg and sprang—yes, sprang, off his injured leg. It must have hurt like hell.

It looked to me like he landed, or rather collided, with the ditch wall about halfway up. He let out a whoop of something that could be pain but also sounded a lot like exhilaration. Franck and I reached down, grabbed his armpits, and dragged him up almost vertically.

I expected him to collapse to the ground in agony, but Robert was made of stronger stuff. The moonlight flashed off his bright white dentures as he grinned. "That was close," he gasped, grinning. "Now it's Bryan's turn!"

My dad cleared the ditch with no problem, like Franck. He was a water-skiing champion in his youth and was annoyingly athletic.

Franck had the foresight to bring his flashlight. It came in handy as we followed him, stumbling across the bumpy, uneven field. Now that I had a moment to collect my thoughts, I became aware of the crickets chirping all around us and the soft, warm air. The scent of wheat fields that had been warmed in the sun during the day made me think of fresh baguettes.

I couldn't quite tell through my rubber boots what I was walking on. In Burgundy it could be anything from old grapevines to a wild boar carcass to Gallo-Roman ruins.

We reached the pile of rocks. Franck's flashlight beam roamed over the specimens.

"Hmm." Robert rubbed his chin. "Just as I thought. Perfection."

The rocks did look large and flat. "How many do you think we'll need?"

"I think twenty should do it," he said. "Let's each choose five, but I get final approval."

We rumbled through the pile of rocks and showed Robert our choices. I went about it gingerly, not relishing the idea of waking a viper family from their slumber.

In the end Robert dismissed almost everything and, of course, chose the winning twenty. It was kind of him to make us at least feel like we had some say.

The big question forming in my mind was how we were going to get the stones plus Robert plus me across the field and the ditch to the car.

I shouldn't have underestimated Franck's ingenuity, however. He and my dad carried most of the rocks, and Franck unearthed an old plank from the tall grasses and lay it across the ditch. It wasn't solid enough for any of us to walk over, but we could slide the rocks across it.

My dad and Franck jumped, holding Robert's arms in between them.

"Teamwork," my dad declared when they landed, triumphant, on the other side.

As we piled the last rock into the trunk of the car, Robert brushed his hands together. "Nothing like a job well done," he said. "I feel like myself again."

With this exploit under my belt, funnily enough, so did I.

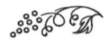

The next morning my dad headed down to Beaune with Franck to meet Robert in the cellar. They were going to unload and install the "salvaged" stones.

They didn't come home for lunch as they took Robert out to celebrate their success. My father was getting in the swing of renovation life in France, which generally included a lot of good food and fine wine.

At around three o'clock Franck called me in Villers-la-Faye. "Can you and your mom pick up the girls from school and come by the cellar? We want to show you what we've done."

"Show off, you mean?"

"Of course!" he answered, unabashed.

I was curious, as well as having a vested interest in the stones I had helped with, so I agreed with Franck's plan immediately.

At four thirty we bundled Clémentine in her little baby car seat, and I drove us to Beaune. When we informed Charlotte and Camille at the door of Saint-Coeur that we were dropping by the cellar on the way home, they both groaned.

"Not again! It's so boring there," Charlotte complained. "It's just rocks and more rocks."

"Yeah," Camille agreed. "Besides, Clémentine just told me she doesn't want to go." Clémentine was wedged beside her two sisters in the back seat, facing backward, and although I couldn't see exactly what was going on, I was fairly certain that six-month-old Clem didn't really hold any strong opinions on the matter.

"It's dirty, too," Charlotte said. "And there are so many spiders."

"It's clean now they've power-washed it. Besides, you like spiders."

"Oh, right," she said. "I forgot."

"Maybe you can collect some and make a spider home for them in the cellar." I knew this idea was perfectly calibrated to capture their imagination.

"*Ouais!*" Charlotte said. "Let's do that, Camille!"

"*Ouais!*" Camille shouted in agreement, then said a few seconds later, "Clémentine says she's changed her mind. She wants to go to the cellar now and collect spiders with us."

I wasn't too certain about that either, but voluntary compliance was never something I questioned.

I managed to secure celebrity parking right across from the cellar. Even with my mom to assist, I had to get Franck to come and help me down with the baby and two overexcited spider-obsessed girls. My mom hated going down the steep, crooked steps, and I was still wary about tripping and dropping the baby carrier. The light emanating from the cellar was even dimmer than usual.

We managed to get to the bottom, and I saw why: the only light turned on was the exposed bulb on the electrical wire.

This didn't stop the girls from running around in the darkest corners looking for spiders, but I feared they were going to take a header and hit one of the shovels or rakes strewn about the cellar floor.

My dad wore a smile that stretched ear to ear and had his hands on his hips.

"Why is it so dark down here?" I said. "I thought we were here to see lights."

"Just you wait," my dad said, his voice replete with anticipation.

"All right!" said Robert, who had retreated to the far corner after giving gallant *bises* and *bonjours* to me and my mom and the girls. "Is everyone ready?"

"Oui!" we all shouted, even though the girls had no idea what they were supposed to be ready for.

Robert flicked the switch. At the bottom of the pillars, and hidden here and there around the cave, lovely golden lights streamed from behind the beautiful ochre rocks we had "acquired" the night before.

My breath caught. Robert was a genius. The effect was stunning. I could finally see just how beautiful the power-washed stones were. The ochre of the local stone complemented the tasting table beautifully. Both it and the lights looked like they'd always been there.

"Magnifique!" I declared.

"Gorgeous!" my mom said. The girls oohed and aahed for a bit, and then, now aided with better lighting, resumed their search for spiders.

"You're brilliant, Robert," I said. "No one would ever imagine it cost us only the price of the cheapest, most basic lights from Bricorama and a covert trip in the moonlight."

I caught a glimpse, for the first time, of what the cellar was going to be. I sent up a little prayer of thanks that Robert had seen it all along.

chapter seventeen

It was December again, and Clémentine was eleven months old. Because she was our third child, we didn't particularly encourage her to become mobile like we had with the other two girls; we knew that meant she could get into exponentially more trouble. She didn't need our encouragement, as it turned out, as she seemed to have inherited Franck's energy and athletic ability.

She was already walking as well as climbing every vertical surface she could find. I would leave the living room for a few seconds and come back to find her on top of the television.

After she fell and hit her head twice on our tile floor, I did what I never thought I'd do as a parent: I bought her a helmet to wear in the house. She didn't like it, but I told myself I was protecting our little Evel Knievel from herself as well as preventable brain injury.

In the months since the great rock heist, things in the cellar had continued to take shape, but Robert had been shipped off unceremoniously for a bit of work in one of the baron's castles in the Loire Valley. We didn't know when he'd be back, but Franck and Hugo carried on as best they could. We all missed him and hoped he'd return sooner rather than later.

Once my parents left for Canada, I got in the habit of taking Clémentine out for walks in her little stroller every day, going through the vineyards and up on Les Chaumes, the commonly owned pastures above the village. I almost always met fellow villagers, like ancient Madame Fribourg, who would examine Clémentine's wee face closely and say, "No mistaking it. She's a

Germain through and through."

Ironic but true. Clémentine continued to be a mini Franck, except much smaller and a girl. Olive skin, almond eyes, a strong, stubborn chin...those same features ran through Franck's grandfather, Pépé Georges; Michèle, Franck's mother; Franck; his brother, Emmanuel-Marie; and now Clémentine.

With Clemmie, our expectations of ourselves as parents were far lower than they'd been with Charlotte and Camille. As long as she was fed, clean, and loved, we figured we were doing fine.

There was no introduction to color cue cards or baby music classes. Those weren't really a *thing* in France anyway. By the third child, it had finally dawned on us that a baby came out the way they came out, and our job as parents was more akin to cruise directors, showing them various possibilities and ensuring their comfort and safety, rather than trying to mold raw clay into a desired shape like a sculptor.

I was so lucky my friend Marie had her fourth child—a daughter named Mahault—just three months before Clémentine. We had each other to call if we were having a bad day, and we enjoyed coffees as Mahault and Clémentine played. That companionship meant everything.

Robert finally returned to Beaune from the Loire, and we celebrated with a lunch at Café de France, a humble bistro just off the ring road around Beaune generally frequented by tradesmen and truckers.

Building wine racks split into several independent compartments that could each be separately locked was turning out to be a difficult proposition. Franck and I had looked, and such a thing did not seem to exist to purchase, yet it was what we needed to be able to rent out the sections separately.

We shared the rack issue with Robert over the bistro's lunch of the day: one of my favorites, *tomates farci*. The clatter around us in the restaurant felt like the ideal backdrop for brainstorming.

I had brought Clémentine, and even though she fussed at first in her stroller, the lovely woman who was the sister of the brother-sister duo who owned and ran the café quickly whisked her away and cuddled her against her impressive bosom. This would have been odd in Canada, but not in France, where children are doted on by pretty much everyone. Our wine might not be safe in an unlocked cellar in Beaune, but our children were safe pretty much everywhere.

As Robert mopped up his *tomates farci* sauce, redolent of onions and ground Charolais beef, with a generous slice of baguette, he said, "I've been lying awake at night thinking of this. Do you know I slept in the castle's dungeon, just for fun?"

"Really?" My imagination was instantly piqued. I wanted to sleep in a dungeon.

"Oh yes, beautiful stonework from the Middle Ages. You would have loved it, Laura. I seemed to be the only one who had any appreciation for it. Anyway, back to the racks. I knew they were the next step, of course. While I was in my dungeon, I thought up a way to build them."

Bien sûr. Of course. I didn't know why we were so lucky to have this knack of meeting the right people at the right time, but I thanked the fates for it.

We spent the next half hour lingering over the cheese platter and listening to Robert's solution. We weren't surprised that it was not only brilliant but also low cost. It was not, however, low effort. Clem, in the meantime, was being passed among the restaurant workers and patrons and admired.

Robert explained that he and Franck would create a rack system out of poured concrete. They would build a series of concrete "shelves," some of which could be covered with nicely painted metal doors and locked, whereas others could be left open.

"We'll make sure to match the concrete to the patina of the stones," he added. "I know a method to do that."

Because Robert was a stickler for doing things the *right* way (i.e., his way, which amounted to the same thing), first he and Franck had to do up a prototype in wood to ensure it would work.

So Franck hustled down to Beaune the next evening, and the two of them whipped together a mock wine shelf in a matter of hours.

Clémentine and I were summoned the next day to give our

opinions on the mocked-up rack. Did it look too imposing? Did it hide the water pipe that ran behind it on that far wall, where we needed water to wash the winetasting glasses? How many could fit side by side? Should we line up the racks against one or two walls?

Clémentine couldn't speak yet, but she did have opinions about the wine rack. She was desperate to climb it or pull it over on herself.

Preventing Clem from doing either of these things was an all-encompassing job and provoked a full-blown toddler moment. Robert seemed to have a plan in mind of exactly how the shelves should be set up. Given the successes of the tasting table and lighting, which still wowed me every time I entered the cellar, I was more than happy to follow his lead.

As Clémentine tried to climb the mock wooden shelf for roughly the sixth time, I gave a final vigorous assent to everything and whisked her home to Villers-la-Faye for an afternoon nap so I could enjoy my sacred coffee and a square of chocolate on the couch. Three children added a new dimension to the chaotic nature of our family life, and I was quickly learning to conserve my energy and pick my battles.

I had Christmas to plan. Robert was hands down the cellar expert, and now that he had returned like the savior he was, I was delighted.

chapter **eighteen**

For the first two weeks in February, Clémentine and I no longer had the house mostly to ourselves during the day. Robert slept in Beaune, but otherwise he basically lived with us at Villers.

He rolled into our driveway in time for morning coffee (he didn't believe in eating breakfast, he had informed us), and by the time I had run the girls to school with Clémentine in her car seat, he and Franck were already deeply engrossed in work.

They set up the concrete molds and pouring station in our garage, which was a smart idea as rain during the winter in Burgundy is unpredictable at best. Our gravel driveway was the grinding station because Robert was a man of precision, and the rough pours needed to be significantly tweaked before they slotted into each other like a very large, unwieldly puzzle.

Many of the concrete sections weighed up to one hundred kilograms, but luckily Franck and Robert were equally what the French term *les forces de la nature*. They both fed off, and actually enjoyed, the physical strain of their project.

In the meantime, I was running out of ideas for what to cook for these two workhorses. Perhaps because he eschewed breakfast, Robert ate like a stevedore at lunch and dinner. I was not used to cooking such vast proportions, and just like any self-respecting Burgundian, I was plagued with nightmares about running out of food.

Robert was also a *fin gourmet*, and although he praised my food unequivocally, he *quand même* always left me with a few tips for improvement. From almost anybody else this would be annoying, but he was helping us so much that I didn't mind...not much, anyway.

The only thing he didn't suggest improvement on was a *tarte tatin* I made on their final day at La Maison des Chaumes, when they took a lunch break from loading the car with the first batch of concrete sections to haul to the cellar for assembly.

Modesty aside, I had knocked the *tarte tatin* out of the park. When Robert licked his lips and said, "That was perhaps the most delicious *tarte tatin* I have ever tasted. Bravo, Laura!" I waited for a few seconds. What was his suggestion for how to improve it? When none came, I grinned like I had won an Olympic medal.

The concrete pieces were moved from Villers to the Beaune cellar—a delicate business as air bubbles, invisible cracks, or the slightest mishandling could cause a segment to break. Miraculously, or more accurately because of Robert's attention to detail, they all arrived intact.

We waited anxiously to find out if the pieces would slide together as Robert had planned. I came down to the cellar to watch the fateful moment. Franck's and Robert's faces were bright red as they slid the first horizontal piece between two vertical rises of shelf. It went in seamlessly.

I was thrilled, but I can't say I was surprised.

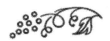

As the gray and fog of winter in the vineyards turned to bright-green leaves and freshly turned dirt, the work in the cellar, now that the shelves were triumphantly assembled, centered around boring but essential tasks such as making sure there was proper water supply and drainage, that the electrical wiring was more or less up to code, and that any wiring that wasn't up to code wouldn't set fire to the entire building above—something we definitely preferred to avoid.

After rebuilding a massive stacked stone wall at a nearby château, Hugo joined us again, and as usual, it was as if no time had passed at all. I had been worried that perhaps he had disappeared because he was scared to be part of another tasting table–type event, but there was no sign of that.

He was thrilled to see the work Robert and Franck had accomplished and marveled at their shelving system. It looked perfect and served our purposes completely.

Hugo helped them mount the metal cages on the squares of wine shelving without cracking the concrete blocks. Hugo insisted I should be the first one to lock a section with a key. After so long, I got goose bumps as I slid the key in the lock. Our cellar dream was finally becoming a reality.

One day I took Clémentine for a walk in Beaune after meeting for coffee at Marie's house. Charlotte and Camille were busy at Saint-Coeur receiving the Catholic education that Robert approved of so thoroughly. They insisted on staying at the school *cantine* that day for lunch because veal dumplings were being served along with chocolate mousse for dessert.

It was a gorgeous spring day, and Clémentine had fallen asleep almost as soon as I gave Marie *les bises* goodbye and began walking into town. My mind wandered to the cellar, and I wondered what Franck, Hugo, and possibly Robert were up to down there. I turned Clem's stroller onto the rue Rousseau Deslandes to see for myself.

Hugo greeted me like a long-lost relative with enthusiastic kisses, one on each cheek. His round and often fierce face changed completely as he cooed over Clémentine and how much she'd grown and how fetching she looked in her pink sun hat.

Franck popped his head out of the cellar just then.

"Laura!" He climbed up to the sidewalk and gave me and Clem a kiss. "This is perfect timing! You're just the person we need. We can't decide on the stair rail."

As much as I was delighted to hear they were finally installing a railing to hang on to while descending the steep, uneven stone stairs, my chest filled with a sense of foreboding. I had just started my walk and was looking forward to continuing. Franck had a knack of innocently hijacking best-laid plans.

I gestured at Clémentine, who had woken up and was now babbling happily as she chewed on the plastic Sophie giraffe that all French parents gave their babies. Sophie was already covered with drool. Clemmie was teething again.

"I'll watch her while you go down," said Hugo. "Babies love me."

I hesitated for a second, but Hugo had chosen that beautiful dress for her, and he was already crouched on the sidewalk in front of Clem's stroller making funny faces that were sending her into paroxysms of giggles.

I followed Franck into the cellar, bending to make sure I didn't bang my head on the stone plinth. A handrail would be a much-needed addition.

My feet crunched in the gravel at the bottom of the stairs, and I glanced around. The cellar was starting to look truly breathtaking, a stark contrast to the dirty, dark, spider-infested place it had been when we'd bought it.

I kissed Robert and the three other men in the cellar, none of whom I knew. They appeared to be different men from the ones who had helped with the tasting table.

The cellar project, Robert, and Franck seemed to be magnets in our little street of Beaune, and I got the feeling a whole lot of people besides Franck and me were invested in the outcome.

Franck introduced me to one of the men who happened to be staying at our apartment above and who definitely didn't fit in with the other men. He was a middle-aged Brit named Rupert who worked in wine imports and was eager to see what all this commotion was beneath the building. He seemed to have the enthusiasm of Fritz the German but perhaps not the same amount of brawn. Indeed, his arms looked like they did nothing more strenuous than tap on a computer keyboard, and his skin was so pale as to be almost translucent.

"I've never actually seen a cellar restored firsthand," he said in a plummy English accent. "It's most edifying. I hope you don't mind, but I've taken lots of photos."

"Go right ahead," I said, waving my arm around the space. "Are you enjoying the apartment?"

"Very much. I plan to use it every time I come to Beaune—they send me here three or four times a year, you know."

"Would you be interested in renting some space to store wine?" Franck asked, ever the salesman.

"Yes," he said. "Actually, I think I would."

I gave Rupert a quick run-down in English about the benefits of renting space in the cellar—how he would have his own key and could entertain clients here with tastings.

He nodded. "That would be quite marvelous. How should I go about securing a spot?"

I reached over and patted Franck's arm. "Franck here can give you all the details, but first, Franck, what's this about a railing?" I asked, mindful of the fact that my baby was out on the sidewalk.

"I don't think you need a railing at all," one of the mystery men piped up.

"I think we do," I argued in French. "After a Burgundian winetasting down here, going up those stairs into the bright sunlight could be hazardous."

The men chuckled.

"Also, you have to remember that many of the people using our cellar will not be from Burgundy," I said. "So they're not used to coming in and out of wine cellars like you all are."

There was a general murmur of assent.

"So what's the issue?" I asked Franck.

Robert appeared beside me holding a mocked-up stair rail made of wood. Of course he had made a mock-up. When did he not execute something perfectly?

"What we can't decide is *gauche ou droite*," he said. Left or right.

"Surely you must have an opinion," I said. I hadn't been spending the past few months with Robert for nothing.

"Of course I do." He winked at me.

"In that case, I choose what you think is best."

He shook his head. "Franck doesn't agree with me, so I suggested we do the gallant thing and let the lady decide."

I sent a questioning look to Franck. Why did he disagree with Robert? Was he in his right mind? I cursed the fact that my husband was an inveterate devil's advocate.

Now the pressure was on. My choice would side with either Franck or Robert. I didn't like this position at all. I sighed and stared at the slabs of stone in the thirteenth-century ceiling, searching for guidance that didn't come. I regretted turning Clem's stroller onto the rue Rousseau Deslandes.

Robert wasted no time in dispatching his helpers to hold the mock-up on the right side of the stairs.

"Why is the rail...curvy?" I asked. It wasn't straight or evenly rounded in an arc; it dipped and waved in a seemingly random pattern.

"I did that on purpose," Robert said. "I've designed it so that if you're going up the stairs and your hand is on the rail, the dips and rises signal when you need to lower and raise your head so as to not bang it on the plinths."

This man's forethought never failed to amaze me.

"I think we should just put it where you think we should put it," I said to Robert, narrowing my eyes at Franck. "You've obviously thought this out."

But Robert clicked his tongue. "No. We decided we need an impartial judge. You're that judge, Laura."

I turned my mind to the problem. The railing on the right side would prevent people (okay, me) from plummeting off the side into the gravel after a few glasses of Gevrey–Chambertin.

However, the railing could just as easily go on the left-hand side closer to the wall. This way, right-handed people could grip it easily as they made their way into Beaune's underworld. Maybe it was less obtrusive and more esthetic this way?

Still, every time I descended into the cellar, I worried about falling off the stairs onto the cellar floor. I took a deep breath and said, "The railing should go on the cellar side, not the wall side."

Robert whooped, and Franck groaned.

Robert kissed my cheek. "You chose correctly!" He raised my

hand in a victory salute. "I knew you would."

Franck raised his palms to accept defeat. "Two against one. I'm outvoted."

I breathed a sigh of relief.

"Wonderful. Now I'm going to get our baby." As I made my way up the soon-to-be railed-in stairs, I could hear Clémentine laughing. Maybe we had not only settled the railing issue but also found the ideal babysitter.

chapter **nineteen**

For the very first time in this cellar project, we had a deadline, and it was a tight one. It was now mid-April. The cellar had to be ready for May seventeenth.

Why do we always do this to ourselves? I wondered. We had set out to renovate the cellar as a side project without a stressful deadline, but somehow we had set up a mad race to the finish line like we had with our La Maison de la Vieille Vigne and the Beaune apartment.

I was starting to wonder if setting a ridiculous deadline was the only way for Franck and me to finish a renovation project, but the added stress came at a bad time.

Clémentine was now fifteen months and bent on trying to maim or kill herself. Taking after her older sisters, her favorite hobbies were trying to eat inedible things, climbing every object she could find, including the corners of the walls, and running away from Franck and me as fast as her chubby little legs could take her. She was adorable, but Franck and I were exhausted.

I had never done particularly well in this stage of parenthood. It had been the same with my first two Houdini daughters. I found babies and older children quite easy, but toddlers left me with the attention span of a gnat and the desire to crawl into bed and sleep for a month. I felt like all I accomplished each day was merely keeping Clémentine alive. On some days even that felt like I barely squeaked through.

I blamed Franck's genes. Not one of my girls was a kid who liked to sit in a corner and play with dolls like I was.

Luckily, my parents were coming back to visit us in May, so help was on the horizon. We wanted them to be able to attend the cellar baptism, so we'd scheduled it for May seventeenth just to add the spice of a deadline to our lives.

When Franck and Robert started discussing the baptism like it was a *fait accompli*, I needed to catch up. I didn't imagine such a thing existed, but I quickly learned that cellar baptisms are a rite of passage in Burgundy, only slightly below baby baptisms in importance.

Franck and I had the habit of getting carried away by our enthusiasm when party planning, and one evening when the combination of fatigue and two glasses of Savigny-les-Beaune made us heady with optimism, we somehow invited thirty people to help us baptize the cellar.

Part of me recognized that it was time. After all, we had started the project when I was pregnant with Clémentine, and now she was inching close to being a year and a half. None of our other projects had lasted this long. It was time for us to finish the cellar and start enjoying it.

A period of intense activity began, and first on the list was to find and install a sink and tap so we could wash tasting glasses without having to haul them up and down those stone steps.

The stair rail was being made, so we could install it on the cellar side of the stairs—as per Robert's and my wishes.

The sink was going to be fixed on the wall where Robert and Franck had put the water pipe, just to the right of the stairs. For the moment, that wall was a long stretch of stone that looked bare in comparison to the other two walls, now lined with concrete wine racks.

We discussed the sink the next time Robert came to Villers for dinner.

Because Robert was Robert, the cellar sink could not be just any sink. I agreed with him. Everything he had done conveyed an atmosphere of stunning authenticity. A white ceramic sink from Bricorama would ruin this effect completely.

Luckily, he had an idea—more than an idea, in fact. He knew the actual exact sink our cellar needed.

"Do you remember how I was in Chablis last weekend?" he asked.

We nodded. He'd grown up there and went back on a regular basis to see family and friends.

"I went to visit an old school chum who runs a *récup*."

I was intrigued. I knew a *récup* was a place where old parts of houses were resold—or sometimes disintegrated. I had heard that such places existed but had never actually been to one. This was not from lack of desire, given my proclivity for old things. I just didn't know where these *récup* sites were or if they were open to the public or just tradesmen.

"I found the perfect sink there," Robert said. "But I need you to come and have a look yourselves."

I wanted nothing better than to visit a *récup*, but I had to look after Clémentine. "I trust you," I said.

Robert wagged his finger, and his dark brows pulled together. "I couldn't possibly overstep in such a way. This is a significant purchase. You must see it and decide for yourselves."

This posed a problem, because I wanted to go with Franck and Robert, but I wasn't sure Clémentine would enjoy the hour and a half drive to Chablis from Beaune, let alone trailing around looking at pieces of old houses. In fact, I was fairly certain bringing her along would be hellish.

Two days later I had solved the problem. I strapped myself into the back seat of our car as Franck set out from the rue Rousseau Deslandes, where we picked up Robert, to Chablis. I was pleased with myself and grateful for Marie, who had offered to take Clémentine for the day.

Clémentine and Mahault would undoubtedly have a grand time, walking, falling down, and fighting over the much-coveted plastic play phone that usually sat on Marie's coffee table. Marie, on the other hand, would have her hands full with two obstreperous and enterprising little girls. *I'll buy her a really nice bottle of Chablis*, I vowed.

Robert was horrified, of course, to find me in the back seat when he came to the car. He tried to convince me to ride in the front beside Franck, feeling it was loutish to make the lady ride in the back.

I stood my ground. I convinced him that in the front seat he and Franck could spend the drive planning the work still left to do. His desire to make the time useful was the only thing that made him concede.

Anyway, he was far better off in the front with Franck. I had not failed to notice he still limped occasionally at the end of the day, and there was far more room to stretch his legs in the front.

Also, I was delighted to be free to daydream as I watched the bright green fields of the Burgundy countryside slide by. I loved the wee stone buildings, all clustered around a church spire, the lazy white Charolais cows that stood chewing grass, and the bright-yellow canola fields that appeared like punches of vibrant sun out of nowhere.

Compared to watching a fifteen-month-old who seemed to be part monkey, the ride felt like a visit to the spa. No bottles to prepare. No diapers to change. No toddler to keep alive. Even though Franck drove like a Formula 1 driver, it was pure relaxation.

The trip went by far too fast. Before I knew it, Robert was directing Franck to a rambling and unkempt stone house on the outskirts of Chablis.

"My friend has a big field behind his house," Robert explained as we pulled up in front. "But you can't see it from the road. *Allez-y.*"

We got out of the car and went through to the back field via a rickety metal gate. Birds chirped and the spring sun warmed my head.

Once we were around the house, my jaw dropped. The massive field was full of huge stones, piles of stone roof tiles, old circular staircases on their sides. It was as if there was once a village of ancient houses and châteaux on this spot, but a malevolent deity had whipped the walls away and left only the insides. I was transfixed.

I began to wander, forgetting about Robert and Franck behind me.

To my right were gigantic blocks of a medieval-looking fireplace. I got a sense of the sheer size the thing would be if it was upright—big enough to roast a massive cow or perhaps even a pair of them.

To my left was a tangle of spiral staircases with fine filigree metalwork. Ahead was the round mass of an old stone well, complete with a bucket on its thick rim. I paused at a pile of oval and circular *oeil de beouf* windows, one of my favorite architectural details in old French houses. *I could spend hours here...days*, I thought.

My path intersected Franck and Robert's again. "Where do all these things come from?" I asked.

"My friend goes to places that are being knocked down or just falling down on their own. He buys little bits of this or that."

I glanced at the massive stairs beside us, which would not have looked out of place in Versailles. Whatever these things were, they were hardly "little."

"He's an eccentric, but he has a good eye," Robert added.

I ran my hand over a stone hump beside me, not quite sure what it was. "I can't believe people don't want these things anymore."

Robert grimaced. "Unfortunately, not everyone values old things as we do, Laura."

Indeed, many French I knew lusted after modern furnishings and houses. Even after three years in France, I still could not understand it when antique armoires and monastery tables were so easy to find.

"Shouldn't we let your friend know we're here?" Franck said, looking uneasily at the house. "He's not the type to come out with a shotgun if he thinks we're trespassing, is he?"

Robert shook his head. "No need to worry about that. He's just a bit of a loner. He keeps a close eye on everything around here. Besides, neither me nor anyone I have ever met has been invited into his house. He'll see it's me, and he'll come out when he's ready. It's best this way, trust me."

"If you say so," Franck said, but he didn't look convinced. He was a stickler for being a polite guest.

"In the meantime"—Robert began walking in another direction and gestured for us to follow him—"let's go and have a look at this sink."

We weaved in and out of the ruins until we reached a patch of the field that seemed to be designated for sinks. All sorts of different, amazing specimens were scattered haphazardly around the tufty weeds and grass.

I leaned down and ran my fingers around the bowl of a perfectly round sink carved from one solid block of stone. It was lopsided and had an incredible patina. Maybe this was the one for us.

Then there was the sink beside it, which was square with a deep trough. That one was incredible, too.

"It's this one." Robert bent over and put his hand on a different sink a few feet away from where Franck and I stood. We joined him in studying it.

It glowed with the ochre tones of local marble and was hewn into a long rectangle with a shallow trough carved into one end.

"What do you think?" Robert asked. "We need something long and shallow for that space, and as soon as I saw this one, I knew it would fit perfectly."

"Do we need to measure it?" Franck dug in his pockets, where he had taken to carrying around a measuring tape.

Robert pursed his lips. "No. I know it will fit. I measured it in my head. The important question is this: Do you approve, Laura?"

"It's beautiful," I said, passing my hand over the aged surface. Where had this sink lived before? Who had used it? It was golden beige, and I could see that it was shot through with pinky streaks. "I fully approve. What do you think it's from?"

Robert shrugged. "I'll ask my friend when he comes out. He'll appear soon."

I wasn't sure exactly how Robert could predict his elusive friend's movements, but maybe he could; they were childhood friends, after all. "What's your friend's name, by the way?"

"His real name is Gilbert," he said. "But everyone calls him le Tortue."

"Le Tortue?" The tortoise. "Why?"

"You'll see," Robert said, cryptic.

As we waited for the Tortoise to appear, I examined our sink some more. "It doesn't look like it came from a château."

"Definitely not," Robert agreed. "It's from a country house. Something humble."

Something simple. I'd always been drawn to simple, whether it was the patina of old pine wardrobes common in French country houses, or traditional French wicker baskets that got even better with age, or the simple Duralex glasses used in school cafeterias all over France.

I admired the plentiful châteaux that dotted the French countryside, but I didn't love them the way I did more rustic places and things. I had never dreamed of living in a château, whereas a rambling old stone farmhouse—*oui.*

I wondered how many generations of people had used this sink. I noticed groves on either side of the hole for the drain, probably from centuries of water wearing away the stone.

When I lifted my head again, emerging from my daydream, a man in a massive wool coat despite the warmth of the spring sun lumbered toward us. His head seemed to disappear into his shoulders, and I could make out no discernable neck. Just like a tortoise. Robert was right. I understood his friend's nickname perfectly.

When le Tortue neared, Robert stuck out his hand and gave him an enthusiastic handshake. Le Tortue grunted a *bonjour*, not even shifting his eyes to Franck or me.

Ever punctilious, Robert introduced le Tortue not by his given name but as "le Tortue." I searched le Tortue's grizzled face for a sign that his nickname bothered him, but he gave none. Maybe he had adopted it as his own and wore it proudly. We shook hands, but le Tortue pulled his away as quickly as possible, clearly not relishing human contact. This close, he smelled of mothballs.

"I'm not going to beat around the bush, mon Tortue," Robert told him. "We're interested in this sink." He gestured at it with a flourish. "But first, the lady would like to know if you are aware of its provenance?"

Le Tortue gave me a long appraising look, then cast an identical look at the sink, apparently impressed by neither. He shrugged after a while. "Nothing special. It came from a farmhouse just outside of Chablis."

"Ah," I said.

"So do you want it?" He was not one to beat around the bush.

"Now, now, mon Tortue." Robert clicked his tongue. "Strive for a little more finesse than that, *mon ami.*"

"How much?" Franck asked. We had pretty much reached the end of our nonexistent budget for the renovation, despite Robert's incredible help. We still had to pay for the cellar baptism. The numbers had somehow increased, and the guest list now stood at about forty. Unfortunately, potluck was not an option in Burgundy.

Le Tortue shrugged again and gave me and Franck a calculating look. "Five hundred euros."

My heart quivered. We didn't have five hundred euros for a sink, but inconveniently I had already managed to fall in love with this one.

Robert burst out laughing and buffeted le Tortue's back with hearty pats. "Ah, my old friend. Have you been into the absinthe again? This early in the morning?"

Le Tortue opened his mouth to protest, but Robert already had his arm slung around his friend's beefy shoulders and was drawing him away. "You can be so silly sometimes," I heard Robert say in a cajoling tone as he led le Tortue out of earshot behind a tangle of metal bannisters.

Franck and I exchanged a look. I for one was quite relieved that Robert had taken the lead in the negotiations, something I never enjoyed. "You like it, too?" I asked in a low voice.

"*Bien sûr,*" he said. "It's perfect. Besides, even if I didn't, if Robert likes it, and you like it, that's good enough for me."

It was several minutes before Robert led le Tortue back. "*Voilà,*" he said. "We've reached an agreement." We waited for a few beats. Robert didn't offer further details, such as the price.

I nodded, not wanting to look over alarmed.

"Also, le Tortue has something to say."

We watched le Tortue, expectant. His head seemed to shrink farther into his shoulders, something I had not believed possible.

"There's a tap," he mumbled.

"Excuse me?" Franck asked. "I'm sorry, I worry I'm going deaf."

"There's a tap that comes with the sink. Do you want to see it? I separated them for sale."

I looked at Robert, and he gave a slight nod.

"Yes. I'd love to see it," I said. "That would be *chouette*."

Le Tortue cast me a suspicious look, then turned and lumbered back to his stone house. I had done it again: freaked out a French person with my Canadian enthusiasm.

"He's a character," Franck observed after le Tortue slammed the door behind him.

Robert chuckled and shook his head. "Le Tortue. He never changes. He's been just like that since elementary school. Can you imagine? Of course all the other kids had him in their sights. Their bullying was relentless. I always stood up for him, though, and let the other kids know that if they messed with him, they would have me to answer to. He's loyal because of that."

I couldn't ask about the final price at this juncture. It seemed like too delicate a moment for mercenary thoughts.

"He was lucky to have you," I said instead.

Robert shrugged. "He's always been an odd character, but he's not so bad. He can eventually be made to see reason, even if he doesn't at first."

We three began to wander around some more, admiring the eclectic collection of pieces le Tortue had collected over the years. "He does valuable work," Robert said. "If he didn't preserve these things, who would? They would be destroyed with the rest of the house in most cases."

It took some time, but le Tortue eventually emerged with a tarnished green copper tap with a fluted animal head I recognized immediately.

"It's a dragon!" I said, delighted. Le Tortue's head raised as he eyed me. *Whoops. That off-putting Canadian zeal again.*

"That's not a dragon," Franck said. "It's a duck. It looks like a mean duck, too, like it might have rabies or something."

"It's a dragon," I insisted. "Who would decorate a tap with a duck?"

"I have seen them actually," offered le Tortue.

"Perhaps," I said. "But this one is definitely a dragon. I'm right. Back me up here, Robert."

Robert nodded. "I must always agree with the lady. *Bien sûr* it's a dragon."

"Robert is so gallant, he would never disagree with you, Laura," Franck pointed out.

"That's true," Robert agreed.

"What about you then?" I asked le Tortue. "You deal with these things all the time. Is it a duck, a dragon, or something else?"

He stared at the tap in his palms with a consternated look as if confronted with a question he had never asked himself before. "I wouldn't hazard a guess," he said finally. "But if you want it, I'll throw it in with the price of the sink."

Franck and I nodded and exchanged a grin. That, we could agree on.

chapter twenty

After paying le Tortue a measly two hundred euros for the sink—Robert was a formidable negotiator, among his multitude of other talents—we spent the afternoon eating a delicious lunch of chicken with cream-and-morel-mushroom sauce and *tropizienne* for dessert at Robert's favorite *routier*, or truck stop restaurant, in Chablis. These places were an inexhaustible source of freshly made home cooking in France.

Next he took us to two cellars of domaines run by his old school friends, and we tasted glass after glass of mineral-rich and delectably dry Chablis wine. We ended up returning to Beaune with the trunk almost dragging on the road from the combined weight of the stone sink and the numerous bottles we had purchased, with a special few for Marie. The day had been an unmitigated success.

Within two days Franck and Robert had installed the beautiful old sink, and that once-empty wall took shape. Franck and I still occasionally debated the duck versus dragon identity of the tap, but that didn't take away from just how perfect the sink looked in the cellar—like it, too, had been there since the thirteenth century. We installed a glass rack above it, and Robert found an old wine barrel somewhere that we put underneath to hide the pipes and give the spot even more decorative flair. *Parfait.*

Franck collapsed beside me on the couch after we got the girls to bed. Clem had recently discovered the trick of catapulting herself out of her crib in the middle of the night, often while still asleep, and Franck and I were both in a deep state of sleep deprivation.

"So your parents' flight gets in at ten o'clock tomorrow morning?" He put his arms around me and pulled me close.

"Yup," I said, nestling against his shoulder. "You sure you don't mind going to pick them up?"

"Of course not, *c'est normal*. I don't want them having to figure out the train from Lyon when they're tired after such a long flight."

"I can't wait to see them," I said. "But the baptism is in a week. We have a ton to do."

Franck smoothed down my hair. "Haven't you learned by now that the two of us can pull off almost anything?"

I chuckled and kissed his neck. "You're not wrong, but we're so tired, Franck. I let the coffee maker run through with just water this morning, and you locked your car keys in the cellar."

"I know, but we'll pull through."

"I guess," I said with a wide yawn.

"There is an important discussion we need to have," Franck said, suddenly serious.

I straightened. "What?" I couldn't for the life of me think what it was.

"Godparents."

"Clem already has godparents." We'd chosen Marie and our friend Martial, and she'd had her baptism in the gorgeous village church of Premeaux-Prissey when she was six months old.

Franck smiled. "Not for Clem, of course. For the cellar."

"The cellar baptism includes godparents?"

Franck shrugged. "*Mais oui*, of course."

And here I was thinking the mere idea of baptizing a wine cellar a bit odd...charming, but odd. "Is this godparent thing just something you made up?" I asked, suspicious.

"Of course not!"

"Are you the godfather of any cellars?" I knew Franck was the godfather of several second cousins' children but had never heard him mention buying Christmas gifts every year for any wine cellars.

He shook his head. "Unfortunately, I haven't been so lucky." He frowned.

I squeezed his thigh. "Then you can be the godfather of our cellar!" I didn't mind. After all, he and Robert had worked so hard and done such an incredible job—way beyond anything I could have imagined when I first ventured down and saw the grungy depths by flashlight.

Franck jerked back. "I could do no such thing. That would be unheard of, like parents making themselves godparents of their own children. There is no need to be a godparent when one is already the parent. Besides, it would take away this honor from someone else."

I chuckled at his reaction. "You take this stuff *seriously*. You'll have to forgive me for not being well versed in the traditions of wine cellar baptisms."

Franck examined my face, then finally his lips quirked up, his humor getting the better of him. He leaned over, gave me a long kiss, and pulled me close again. "I suppose it's not your fault you're a heathen foreigner. Anyway, you know I would forgive you anything."

I did know, and though I didn't feel I had much to be forgiven for—except perhaps excessive control needs and an occasional lapse of faith that things would turn out—I was grateful for it. I thought about godparents for a bit. "If it can't be you, it should be Robert," I said. "Nobody deserves it more than him."

Franck kissed the top of my head. "That is exactly what I think. You don't think your dad would be upset?"

"Of course not. He loves the cellar project, but he's not a religious person, so I don't think it would mean much to him. As long as he can store his wine in there and have a key, and take part in our celebration, he'll be thrilled. I guarantee it."

Franck let out a sigh of relief. "Thank goodness. It's true that he's a very fair-minded person, and he has seen what Robert has done... It has to be Robert, *bien sûr*, but I just hate the idea of offending anyone."

"You won't," I said. "I promise."

"I was thinking we could make your mother godmother," Franck added.

I thought about it and realized Franck had hit on the perfect solution to honor Robert and make my parents feel completely included.

"You're brilliant," I said.

Franck smiled. "I'm not, but sometimes I have good ideas."

"So what exactly does this baptism ceremony involve?" I asked.

"We have to do it in the cellar," Franck said. "Then we can do the meal here at Les Chaumes afterward. It requires a speech, a special wine opening, and a ceremonial toast."

"What special wine opening?" I asked, intrigued, but at the same time I was barely able to keep my eyes open. I felt so warm beside Franck, and Clem was surely going to catapult out of her crib before too long…

"You'll see," Franck said. A few moments later he shook my shoulder. "I'm going to get you to bed. You need to sleep. I'll put Houdini back in her crib tonight."

Two days after my parents arrived, and only three days until the baptism that Sunday, my mom and I went to the cellar with the girls after school. It had become a fun place for the girls now. For one thing, Hugo and Robert were two of their favorite people, and second, it resembled a magical underground kingdom.

Their favorite game was pretending they were orphans in Paris and they had discovered the cellar and made it their new home. Clémentine was the baby they found on top of the Eiffel Tower and had to take care of. Charlotte and Camille were better at keeping Clem occupied than I was, so I was more than happy with their imaginary game.

Once we arrived and greeted Franck, Robert, Hugo, and my

dad, Franck handed my mom and me an armful of artistically rendered false ivy vine.

"Your dad and I have been trying all afternoon to put this up to cover that pipe," Franck said. "But we're both equally as useless at it. Could you two give it a try?"

I looked up in the far-right corner of the cellar, where a large gray plastic pipe, necessary for water, was the only thing that marred the beauty everywhere the eye fell.

Robert and Hugo were busy piling empty wine bottles that Robert had sourced God knows where in the gaps between the cellar sections and positioning back lighting so when we turned on the cellar lights, they would glow green.

"We can try," I said. I glanced over to see Clémentine happily being dragged around by her big sisters. They knew not to let her pop the gravel in her mouth. Franck set up a stepladder by the pipe, and my mom stayed on the ground due to her vertigo, while I climbed up like a monkey and she passed me the start of the vine.

For the next half hour, I was engrossed in my task weaving the ivy around the pipe so it was neither too tight nor too loose but looked natural, like it had grown there (impossible, of course, in a cellar with no natural light, but verisimilitude didn't seem to matter as much as hiding the PVC).

I finished and put my hands on my hips to observe my work from the ladder, checking to see if any final tweaks were required.

I looked around for the men to get their opinion and saw Franck and my dad each carrying an end of a huge carton with "Nabuchodonosor" stenciled in black on the side.

"Is that what I think it is?" I asked from the top of the ladder. "Also, where did Clémentine, Charlotte, and Camille go?" My chest clenched. The street above was narrow and people drove fast.

"Hugo took them to buy *pains au chocolat* at the boulangerie, and yes, this is what you think it is."

I let out a squeal of excitement and scrambled down to the gravel.

"What is it, Laura?" my mom asked.

"It's a Nabuchodonosor, a *massive* bottle of wine."

"That's a bottle of wine?" she asked in disbelief. "Just one bottle?"

We went to the tasting table as Franck and my dad gingerly took it out of the box to stand it on the table. My mom gasped. It towered over all of us.

"How many bottles of wine fit in there?" she said.

"Twenty." I had made it my business to memorize the progression of wine bottle sizes during my first year in Beaune when I was eighteen. They went from a quarter bottle (called "a quarter") to a Midas (forty bottles).

This was a bottle of Savigny Les Guettes, a truly magnificent wine made by one of Franck's many distant family members.

Robert was already pacing around the table with his hands clasped behind his back, admiring the bottle from all angles. "Now *that*," he declared finally, "is a bottle worthy of baptizing this cellar."

That night at our house in Villers, we debated the official name of the cellar. Franck and Robert were adamant: the cellar had to have an official name in time for the baptism.

"Otherwise it would be like baptizing an unnamed child," Robert said, taking another bite of homemade quiche Lorraine for emphasis.

"Le Cave de Robert," I suggested. "Robert's Cellar." It would certainly be well-served.

"*Surtout pas!*" Robert's brows snapped together. "It is not my cellar. That would be misleading."

I understood this was not a subject to be joked about with Robert.

"Le Cave Beaunois?" I suggested. "No, scratch that. There are hundreds of cellars in Beaune. Too ubiquitous."

"Why don't you just call it le Cellier du Vieux Beaune?" my

mom suggested. "You called the apartment above le Relais du Vieux Beaune, and I always think of the two going together."

Franck bit his lip, nodding slowly.

"I like it," I said. "I don't know why we never thought of that."

Our eyes turned to Robert. If he didn't like it, we would have to think of something else. This cellar was as much his now as it was ours, even if he didn't see it that way.

His dark eyes gave nothing away, but slowly he reached out and raised the glass of Ladoix-Serrigny in front of him.

"To le Cellier du Vieux Beaune!" he declared, using every ounce of gravitas in his naturally bass voice. *"Santé!"*

We raised our glasses to join his in the cheer. Our cellar was ready to be baptized.

chapter twenty-one

Even though the cellar baptism was the next day, and we had masses of things to do in Villers-la-Faye, my mother, the girls, and I hit the Saturday morning market in Beaune. The earth would have to grind to a halt for us to miss it. Besides, it was a bright-blue May morning. The leaves had unfurled on the *tilleuls* around the Place Carnot and were now a bright, vivid green. Fresh flowers had been planted everywhere, and the swallows swooped from the tiled rooftops.

First we placated the girls, whom I had started collectively referring to as "the Bevy," with numerous rides on the merry-go-round in the Place Carnot. Clémentine was now as addicted as her sisters, and their favorite thing was to squeeze her between them in the Cinderella-esque carriage and pretend they were all princesses.

After that we headed to the *brocante* tables on the other side of the Place. Charlotte and Camille each held one of Clem's hands, which meant she couldn't climb, grab, or eat anything illicit.

We browsed the eclectic collection of antiques at the tables: an oil painting of a voluptuous woman getting out of the bath, a massive brass corkscrew, old cow bells, and an old statue of Saint-Vincent, the patron saint of winemaking.

"That's it!" I said to nobody in particular.

"What?" My mom sidled up beside me, where I stood contemplating Saint Vincent.

"This is what the cellar needs—its very own saint."

"I think you've been living with a Catholic for too long," my mom said.

"No, no, it's not like that." I pointed at the statue, about six inches tall and made of cream-colored stone. "That is Saint Vincent, the patron saint of winemakers. Don't you think it would be lucky to have him in the cellar?"

"Like a talisman?" my mom asked.

"Exactly."

"How much?" I asked the seller, and a few minutes later, I had purchased a Saint Vincent of our own.

We decided to take it right to the cellar, where Franck, Robert, and my dad were, before we continued with the food shopping portion of our market outing.

"Salut!" I called out as we made our way down the open stairs. The girls clattered down with no issues now, but every time I descended, I appreciated the cleverness of Robert's curvy metal railing.

Hugo was there, too, so we engaged in an affectionate round of *bises* before I could explain why we had stopped by.

Franck, Robert, and my dad were standing somewhat awkwardly between the stairs and the sink, and they didn't seem inclined to move. I had no idea what that was all about, but first things first.

"Look what I found for our cellar!" I brandished my statue and quickly unwrapped it to unveil Saint Vincent for the men. "Our very own Saint Vincent! Won't he look fabulous in the cellar?"

Robert let out a puff of breath. "Brilliant, Laura. I can't believe I didn't think of a Saint Vincent myself. Of course every Burgundian cellar should have one."

I shrugged, a warm blush stealing across my cheeks. "Well, I was thinking... Baptism, saints, wine... You know."

Franck didn't come over to give me a kiss as he normally would; he merely nodded. "It's perfect, *mon amour.*"

I scanned the cellar, looking for a random outcropping of rock or a shelf where our saint could live. "Where should we put it?" I wondered out loud.

Hugo, the only man who wasn't nailed to the spot by the stairs, stepped over and took it from me. "I'll find a pedestal for it," he assured me. "You just leave him with me, Laura. I'll make sure he looks perfect."

I smiled at Hugo. "*Merci.*" I knew I could trust Vincent in Hugo's capable hands.

My gaze shifted back to the three men by the stairs. "Now, will you explain why the three of you are standing there like your feet are glued to the ground?"

They shared complicitous looks. "It's a surprise," my dad said finally.

"It was Robert who did it late last night," Franck added. "But we weren't planning on any of you seeing it until tomorrow."

My dad and Franck looked at Robert, who seemed to be mulling something over. Finally, he waved his hand. "*Ce n'est pas grave,*" he said. "The girls are all here, and it's a surprise for them, after all."

I racked my brain, but I couldn't begin to imagine what he was talking about.

"Come over here, girls," I called to them. They were clustered in the far corner, already deeply engaged in their imaginary orphan game.

"We're busy!" Camille called back.

"It's for a surprise!"

In less than three seconds, the Bevy was at my side.

"Surprise?" Camille and Clem said, and Clem was jumping around in her little overalls, excited because her sisters were excited.

"*Oui,*" Robert took the lead and bent down to the girls' level. "I had an idea yesterday. I was thinking, you and your friends will be using this cellar when you come for family parties or wine tastings."

The girls nodded solemnly, Clem included.

"None of you can reach the tasting table, am I right?"

Charlotte and Camille shook their heads. They were far too short. Clémentine shook her head, too, and burst out laughing. I didn't think she was following Robert, but she was certainly enjoying herself.

"That's not really fair now, is it?" he continued.

They shook their heads again.

"It is your family cellar after all, so I thought you girls needed a tasting table of your own so you can properly enjoy it."

He looked to Franck and my dad. "Gentlemen," he said and made a sweeping gesture with his arm.

They men stepped away, revealing the most perfect little tasting table that was just the right height for the girls.

I gasped. When had he made this, and how?

The girls shrieked with delight. The base was made of local marble. On top was a miniature wine barrel that Robert had no doubt salvaged from one of his numerous sources. On top of that was a thin piece of marble for the tabletop.

A bottle of Orangina and three small glasses were laid out on top.

To think Robert had done this... Tears pricked at the corners of my eyes.

I gave him the *bises* and thanked him, then thanked him again, but the sound of my gratitude was lost in the delighted glee of the girls conducting their first tasting in Le Cellier du Vieux Beaune.

I didn't go back until the next day for the ceremony. Heading into the cellar, I paused for a moment on the stairs to take in the beauty below me.

We were so lucky. Fate had thrown us the cellar in the first place, and it turned out to be a place that had potential to turn into...this. Robert had appeared in our lives like some sort of angel from wine-cellar heaven and ushered us through every step in the restoration. Sometimes it was still hard to believe the stars had aligned so perfectly.

Something new on the wall just to the right of the stairs caught my eye. Hugo had been true to his word, and now Saint Vincent stood proudly on a gorgeous stone plinth mounted on the wall, guarding the cellar for the years to come.

Like everything else Robert, Hugo, and Franck had done, Saint Vincent had a timelessness about him, like he belonged in this cellar, like he had always lived here.

The children's table was all set up with sparkling apple juice and little glasses, and Charlotte and Camille quickly took Clem over and assumed their roles as hostesses for all their friends, many of whom were already chattering about. For most of them, a thirteenth-century cellar was nothing extraordinary.

Within half an hour the cellar was fuller with people than I'd imagined it could be—friends, family, guests from our properties. We served fresh *gougères* made by André, cubes of Comté cheese, and little rounds of *saucisson sec* from chez Raillard in the rue Pietonne. Accompanying that were bottles of gorgeous white Grand Cru Chablis that Robert had picked up in his hometown and a generous supply of Naudin-Ferrand's Haute-Côtes de Beaune, as well as the massive Nabuchodonosor, which Robert and my mother, as godparents of the cellar, had ceremoniously uncorked. It took two people to hold the massive bottle while glasses were poured.

The decibel level was high, and everyone was laughing and chatting. After a time, Franck put his fingers to his mouth and let loose a wolf whistle so shrill and commanding that it surprised even me, and I had been married to him for many years. I didn't know he could do that.

You could have heard a pin drop. He cleared his throat. I knew Franck hated public speaking, in the same way he knew I hated physical challenges such as jumping over ditches.

"I just wanted to say a few words." He gave a lovely speech that sang the praises of Robert and Hugo, and named my mother and Robert as godparents of the cellar. We raised a glass both to them and to all our friends and family who continued to support our crazy exploits with aplomb.

I was probably the only one who could tell he was nervous from the slight tremble in his hand as he held his wineglass.

When he was done, we shared an intimate smile. I grinned

across the cellar and gave him a little thumbs-up to let him know he had done brilliantly, and he smiled his relief.

I began to sing the "Ban Bourgignon" because I was in an extremely celebratory mood and also because I knew Franck would be grateful to have the attention shifted from him quickly.

Everyone joined in, and we sang it several times. All the children clustered around their tasting table knew exactly what to do, and even Clémentine, standing there beside her sisters in her lilac party dress, turned her little hands to the singing like a true *bourgignonne*, born and bred.

The feast at the house afterward was an epic sit-down affair. We had moved most of the furniture out of the living room and set up long trestle tables in a huge L shape. We somehow managed to sit forty people.

I spent a lot of time traipsing in and out of the kitchen, and Marie was right by my side helping me. Franck was of course occupied with serving everyone wine, and Robert was busy regaling the assembled company with racy Burgundian drinking songs that got racier as more wine was consumed. Laughter and the sound of children filled the house.

I leaned against the door of the kitchen wiping a dish with a towel while I watched, amused, Robert singing his latest song. Not surprisingly, he had a beautiful deep singing voice. He was a true Renaissance man.

I felt Franck come up behind me. I turned slightly to see he was holding Clémentine in one arm, who was chewing the end of a baguette.

"We did it." He kissed my neck. "We did it *all*."

I couldn't argue. The baby, the cellar... It had all turned out, despite the moments of stress and fatigue. It had turned into this, a wonderful celebration of life and wine and history and solidarity.

"We did," I agreed with a smile. "Again. This is becoming something of a pattern with us."

Franck shrugged, and Clem began to laugh out of the blue. Franck gave her a kiss on the forehead. "I promised that if we got married, it would never get boring."

"You've definitely fulfilled that."

Franck's eyes shifted to our third daughter. "You do your part as well."

I laughed. "I guess I do."

La Fin

Interested in seeing photos of the wine cellar restoration in Beaune and checking out that marble tabletop for real? Download my personal photo album here: https://bit.ly/2P21dpZ

I would love to hear what you thought of *My Grape Cellar*. The easiest way to give feedback is to leave a review on Amazon. I appreciate each and every one!

the grapevine

Interested in receiving Laura's French recipes, sneak peeks at her new work, as well as exclusive contests and giveaways, insider news, plus countless other goodies? Sign up for Laura's Grapevine newsletter and join our *fantastique* community.

http://bit.ly/LauraBradburyNewsletter

If you enjoyed *My Grape Cellar*, then you will love my other bestselling escapist memoirs, the Grape Series.

Turn the page for an excerpt of *My Grape Year*, voted number one in Buzzfeed's "18 Feel-Good Books That Will Make You Believe in Love."

Sneak peek of
Chapter One
My Grape Year

At the age of seventeen in a last-minute twist of fate, Laura Bradbury is sent to Burgundy, France, for a year's exchange. She arrives knowing only a smattering of French and with no idea what to expect in her first foray out of North America. With a head full of dreams and a powerful desire to please, Laura quickly adapts to Burgundian life, learning crucial skills such as the fine art of winetasting and how to savor snails.

However, the charming young men of the region mean Laura soon runs afoul of the rules, particularly the no-dating edict. Romantic afternoons in Dijon, early morning *pain au chocolat* runs, and long walks in the vineyards are wondrous but also present Laura with a conundrum: How can she keep her hosts happy while still managing to follow her heart? Follow along on Laura's journey to *l'amour* in *My Grape Year*.

chapter one

1. No Drinking
2. No Drugs
3. No Driving
4. No Dating

By signing this contract, I hereby accept my role as Ursus Youth Ambassador for the 1990–1991 exchange year abroad and agree to abide by all four of the "Rules for Exchange Students."

The other outbound exchange students around me were scribbling their signatures on the forms.

No Drinking. I knew I was heading to Europe, Switzerland, if everything went according to plan, and even though I was drawn by the history and beauty and exoticism, I was also hoping to be able to enjoy a nice glass of beer or wine from time to time. I was seventeen and would be graduating from high school in three short months, so I hoped they wouldn't take this rule too seriously in what my grandmother always referred to as "the old country."

No Drugs. I seriously doubted that marijuana was as ubiquitous in Europe as it was on Vancouver Island, Canada, where it self-seeded in many people's back gardens. And since I had no intention of ever trying any other type of drug, this rule wasn't an issue.

No Driving. It would be weird to no longer be able to drive nor enjoy the independence that came with that. Still, like many

Canadians, I knew how to drive only an automatic and didn't like traffic very much, so I could live with this rule.

No Dating. This rule bothered me the most. It had just been explained to us that as Ursus Youth Ambassadors we would have to be available and open to all people we encountered during our year abroad. Having an exclusive romantic relationship would interfere with that goal. Also, the Ursus Club hosting us would be responsible for our welfare during our year in its country, and that would be far simpler to ensure when we students remained single. I could see the logic of it all, but my romantic life during my high school years had been seriously disappointing, if not to say practically nonexistent. My heart longed for romance and love.

Still, I felt as if the whole world was out there waiting for me, and I needed to take the step to meet it. If that meant signing this contract, then I would do whatever it took.

I picked up my pen and signed my name.

The men's polyester pants were off-gassing in the stuffy hotel room. The scorched smell of synthetic fabric tickled my nostrils. March was generally a cool month in Victoria, so the hotel staff hosting the annual Ursus District Convention hadn't anticipated the heat wave. The Rotary and Lions clubs, similar community service organizations, had recently begun to welcome female members, which I was sure had lessened the polyester quotient. Ursus, though, stubbornly remained a men-only group, aside from their female International Youth Exchange Ambassadors like me.

A makeshift fan had been unearthed and stuck in the corner of the room, but sweat trickled inside my navy wool blazer, which had already been festooned with at least forty pins. Pins were the currency of the incoming and outgoing exchange students and were traded with the fervor of stocks on Wall Street.

The interview was almost over, thank God. If they liked me, I would get the final confirmation that I would be spending the

1990–1991 academic year as an exchange student in what I hoped would be my first choice of host country, Switzerland. There was only one available spot in Switzerland, and it was contested hotly every year. Belgium, my second choice, was better than nothing. Germany was my third choice, but I knew I definitely didn't want to end up in Germany. I'd never found blond men attractive, and I vastly preferred wine to beer. It was a crime that Italy, France, and Spain weren't options. I could completely envision myself at some Spanish or Italian bar, dancing on the tables after a night fueled by sangria or Prosecco—though I'd apparently signed away my rights to drink either of these.

"I see Switzerland was your first choice, Laura," the head of the committee observed.

Was? Not is?

Every one of the ten or so men around the table had a copy of my application in front of him. "Can you explain your reasons for that?"

I had answered this question so many times in previous interviews that I could do it in my sleep. "One of my main motivations for going on a year abroad is to learn a foreign language," I said. "Switzerland has not one but *three* official languages—French, German, and Italian. I would love to be exposed to more than one language during my year as an Ursus Youth Ambassador." Actually, I was hell-bent on a year abroad because I sensed this huge, marvelous world waiting for me beyond the mossy shores of my island home, and I vibrated with the need to meet it.

The Ursunian who was chairing the interview cleared his throat. "That is an excellent answer, Miss Bradbury. However, we just received the news that the Switzerland spot was nabbed by another district." The men exchanged shocked looks at this breach of fair play.

What? What about my fantasies of racing up and down the Swiss hills like Maria from *The Sound of Music* and warming myself up with some lovely cheese fondue and wine in a wooden chalet afterward, preferably with an entourage of handsome Swiss men? I knew I would have to deal with my disappointment later; right then wasn't the time. I dug my nails into my palms and smiled brightly. "I'll go to Belgium, then."

"We do have several spots there. I just feel we should let you know, though, that more than half of them are in the Flemish-speaking part of Belgium."

Flemish? I had been so sure I was going to Switzerland that I hadn't even considered the possibility of being sent to Flemish-speaking purgatory.

I flashed another smile. "Of course, I would make the most out of any placement," I said. "However, French is Canada's second official language, and growing up here on the West Coast, I have always regretted the fact that I have never learned to speak it fluently. I hope to go to McGill University in Montreal, so obviously French would be a huge advantage for me."

There was no need to mention that French had actually been my worst subject all through high school, and that I'd had to drop it after Grade 11 because it was torpedoing my GPA. Or that I ran out to the quad after my Grade 11 provincial exam for French and yelled, "Thank God! I will *never* have to speak French again in my life!"

A slighter, bald man piped up. "You may not be aware of this, Miss Bradbury, but there is no way for us to guarantee where you will be placed. We send over the files for the incoming students, and it's up to our Belgian brothers to allocate them as they see fit."

I struggled to maintain my bright-eyed demeanor.

"There's always France, I suppose," mused the head man, as though thinking aloud.

My head snapped in his direction. "I understood there were no exchange spots available in France."

He cleared his throat. "That *was* the case, but there has been a...ah...development."

My heart began to somersault. *France?*

A tall man at the opposite end of the table, who had been picking something fascinating out from under his thumbnail, jerked his head up. "With good reason!" he said, paying attention now. "Every exchange we arranged in France has ended in disaster. The families didn't even bother to come and pick up our students from the airport, or they suddenly decided that they were sick of hosting and locked the child out of the house or left on vacation without them. We couldn't possibly jettison another student into—"

The chair cleared his throat meaningfully. "I have a letter here from the Ursus Club in Beaune, France." He waved the letter, which from what I could see was written in elaborate cursive with a fountain pen. I longed to get a closer look—it possessed a tantalizing whiff of the exotic. "They say that one of their students is being hosted this year by our district, so they would welcome one of our students. Just one student, you see. It would be on a trial basis. They sound sincere."

"Don't believe them," snarled the tall man. "I was president of our club the year our poor student was abandoned at the airport in Paris. He had to take a plane back to Seattle the next day. Try explaining *that* to his parents!"

"We must believe them," the chair insisted. "Ursus spirit demands we have good faith in our French brothers. Besides, Miss Bradbury here strikes me as a competent sort of person who can deal with extreme situations. I wouldn't even mention the possibility of France to most of our outgoing students."

"I—I..." I stuttered, wondering how I was going to disabuse him of this notion. I couldn't imagine any horror worse than leaving for a year abroad only to have to return to Canada the next day with my tail between my legs. Yet...France! I had always wanted to see Paris and the Eiffel Tower and learn how to drape scarves properly.

"George"—the tall man's voice was stiff with displeasure—"throwing this nice young lady here to the French would be like throwing a lamb to the wolves, and I for one—"

"Neil," the head man said in a quelling tone, "there is an open space for France, and it needs to be filled. Miss Bradbury has explained how urgently she wants to learn French. She is mature and full of positive energy. I have complete confidence in her."

What is the word for "shit" in French? Merde? My mind whirred as I tried to find a way to extract myself from this fix.

But then I thought about red wine. Little cafés. Baguettes.

French men were supposed to be very charming, weren't they? In any case, they had to be an improvement on Canadian boys. It could be a disaster, or it could be even better than Switzerland. In any case, I decided, it was definitely better than spending a year learning Flemish.

"I'd be delighted to take that spot in France." I straightened my shoulders.

All the men except Neil nodded approvingly at me as though I had just performed a selfless and heroic act. Darn. Had I?

The chair erased Switzerland and Belgium from my application and wrote "FRANCE" on it in large capital letters. He scrawled something in his notes.

"That settles it, then! You'll be heading to France in August, Miss Bradbury. I hope you have an excellent year, or shall I say a *bon voyage*?" He chuckled at his own joke.

"Thank you," I said, "or shall I say *merci*?" This got a laugh out of all the men, and they stood up and stretched their polyester-clad legs to indicate that I was dismissed.

I must have missed the sound over the whir of the fan and the muffled scrape of chairs against the carpet, but when I think back to it now, I am convinced there must have been a mighty creak. There had to have been, because at that precise moment my entire life shifted on its axis.

To purchase
My Grape Year
https://bit.ly/2Y2w9uy

a conversation with **laura bradbury**

Why is *My Grape Cellar* shorter than the other Grape books?

After finishing my first novel, *A Vineyard for Two*, I needed a smaller project as a bit of a palate cleanser. *A Vineyard for Two* was a massive learning curve, and I had to teach myself how to write fiction as I wrote it. Afterward, I was creatively drained, but at the same time I felt like I'd been neglecting my Grape Series for too long.

I have long had the idea for *My Grape Cellar* floating around in my head, but it was a different kind of project from my other Grape books in that the renovation lasted over three calendar years instead of spanning a shorter period like the others. How would I fit this into a book? I wondered. Something the size of a novella felt just right. I have a few Grape stories in my head that, like this one, don't justify a full-length book but still tell an important part of the overall Grape story.

I set out to write a 20,000-word novella but ended up with almost 40,000 words. Anyone who knows me won't be too surprised!

The next book in the Grape Series is *My Grape Québec*, which tells the story of Franck's arrival to join me in Montréal. It slots in between *My Grape Year* and *My Grape Paris* (I know, I know... There I go writing out of order again! I am incorrigible.) It will be a standard Grape book in that it spans a full year and a regular novel length.

Was it strange writing a book that didn't fit into a calendar year?

It was quite different, and there were certain aspects of the story of *My Grape Cellar*, such as convincing Franck to have a third child, my pregnancy, and Clémentine's arrival into the world, that

I purposely glossed over. This is because I am going to delve into them in detail in the upcoming Grape books *My Grape Town* and *My Grape Baby*. I didn't want to use all that material in this book; I just wanted to refer to those events as things going on in our lives at the time. Technically that was a bit tricky.

It was slightly more difficult with *My Grape Cellar* to remember the sequence of events than in my year-long books. Luckily, I wrote a blog at the time, which I can still access. That allowed me to date and sequence the cellar restoration with accuracy. I was so grateful to my past self for doing this! I remember at the time wondering vaguely why I was bothering given I was so busy, but now I am thankful. Sometimes we are way smarter than we realize!

Do you still own your wine cellar? How do you use it?

We do! In fact, Franck is in France as I write this, replacing light bulbs and doing the yearly maintenance there. I will be leaving for Burgundy in a few days to do the principle photography for my upcoming cookbook based on the Grape Series. We will do several tastings in our cellar for Rebecca, my coauthor and wonderful photographer. It is just the most amazing, atmospheric, historical place for winetastings.

When we're in France, which will be with increasing frequency as our daughters grow older, we use the cellar often to entertain friends, family, and guests at our vacation rentals. We also continue to rent space for people to age their wine. It is an incredibly special spot.

What happened to Robert?

The incredible Robert! He absolutely refused to take payment for his help, so instead we bought him and his lovely wife, Mireille, tickets to visit us in Canada. We had a wonderful time with them, fishing for salmon in the Pacific, hiking, going out for meals, and just generally having a blast.

They stayed at a friend's house right on the beach in Victoria. When the friend came home from vacation, he found that Robert had completely reorganized his tool room, improving it immensely, and fixed numerous items such as squeaking doors. Knowing Robert, that did not surprise me one bit.

We love seeing Robert whenever he can make it to Burgundy from Brittany, and we have enjoyed a lasting friendship.

With someone like Robert appearing at the right time, do you believe in luck or hard work?

I am a true believer in luck. Although we can make ourselves open to it, I think it is distributed in a completely random way. Also, it is not necessarily given to the deserving.

When I was so ill with PSC prior to my transplant, I had a lot of people tell me I should try to manifest better health and a positive outcome. Don't even get me started on all the ill-advised suggestions for cucumber juice cleanses, weird herbs, and visiting an (expensive) shaman. I don't believe any of that crap. People in my PSC family were better educated, more positive, and manifested harder and did not survive. It is sheer luck that one of my cells didn't go rogue and become cancer and that I pulled through the transplant with only treatable complications.

It is an exquisitely harmful brand of cruelty to sick people to suggest we can control our destiny and simply choose to be healthy. So as a result I am a big believer in luck. We were so lucky to befriend Robert.

discussion guide

1. How do you feel when you see ancient things—buildings, art, objects?

2. If you were to write a memoir about only a small slice of your life, which slice would you choose? Where would it begin and end?

3. Have you been to a winemaking region in Europe? What intrigued you there?

4. Have you ever embarked on a project that felt daunting at the start? How did you manage it? Did it turn out?

5. What region of France would you like to visit?

6. Have you worked together with a life partner or good friend on a large project? What were the positives or negatives of working with someone you were close to?

7. When making a decision, do you tend to think everything through logically, or do you just leap and hope the net will appear?

8. Have you ever had a person like Robert appear in your life at just the right time and place? Who was it, and in what circumstances?

about laura

Laura Bradbury is the author of five bestselling memoirs. *My Grape Cellar* is the sixth book in her romantic, escapist Grape Series. Her novel *A Vineyard for Two* was published in 2019.

Laura published her first book—a heartfelt memoir about her leap away from a prestigious legal career in London to live in a tiny French village with her Burgundian husband in *My Grape Escape*—after being diagnosed with PSC, a rare autoimmune bile duct/liver disease. Since then she has published five more books in the Grape Series about her enchanting adventures in France. *A Vineyard for Two* was her debut in fiction.

Now living and writing on the West Coast of Canada with a new liver and three Franco-Canuck daughters (collectively known as "the Bevy"), Laura runs three charming vacation rentals in Burgundy with her husband, does all she can to support PSC and organ donation awareness, and speaks on creativity, fear, and moving toward life no matter what. She writes about all these things in her blog. She is working on the two sequels to *A Vineyard for Two* in her Winemakers Trilogy, more Grape Series books, and a cookbook based on the Grape Series, due in fall 2020 from Touchwood Editions.

find **laura** online

The Grapevine Newsletter
http://bit.ly/LauraBradburyNewsletter

Website
www.laurabradbury.com

Facebook
facebook.com/AuthorLauraBradbury

Twitter
twitter.com/Author_LB

Instagram
instagram.com/laurabradburywriter

Pinterest
pinterest.ca/bradburywriter

BookBub
bookbub.com/authors/laura-bradbury

Goodreads
goodreads.com/LauraBradbury

Books by Laura Bradbury

The Winemakers Trilogy
A Vineyard for Two

The Grape Series
My Grape Year
My Grape Paris
My Grape Wedding
My Grape Escape
My Grape Village
My Grape Cellar

Other Writings
Philosophy of Preschoolers

Made in the USA
Columbia, SC
25 October 2020